MORE PRAISE FOR THE SECRET LIFE OF CLOWNS

"*The Secret Life of Clowns* is a lively, informative and engaging book. Jeff Raz writes from the heart and tells much of what he knows from his four decades as a performer in a way that readers will be able to follow and enjoy."
> —**Joel Schechter, D.F.A.,** *author of* Durov's Pig: Clowns, Politics, *and* Theatre and The Pickle Clowns: New American Circus Comedy *and Professor of Theatre at S.F. State University*

"A spot-on account of the insecurities, the flops and the triumphs of a student of clown, whether in school or in the biggest circus in the world. It brought a lot of memories back, both as a clown with Cirque du Soleil and as a student of clown. I liked being reminded of the unknowns of it all, when it looked impossibly bigger than life. For an old clown, it jogs memories; for a new one, it's insightful and affirmative to the challenging rites of passage."
> —**Mooky Cornish,** *star of Cirque du Soleil's* Vareki

"Jeff Raz has written a fun, informative read, an up-close-and-personal look at what it is to train as a clown, to teach clowning and to clown in one of the most renowned circuses in the world. This book is also chock-full of asides on the history of clowning, clown trivia and profiles of unique clowns. Could there be a more comprehensive take on the life of clowns?"
> —**Melissa Smith,** *Conservatory Director at the Tony award winning American Conservatory Theatre*

"Jeff Raz taught me that the performing arts are a business, that I should be vulnerable on stage but not when it comes to the business side. Without him I never would have had the courage to move to Dubai and launch *Dubomedy*."
> —**Mina Liccione,** *star of* Stomp, *Clown Conservatory graduate and founder of the premiere comedy school in the Middle East*

"What is a clown? And if you think you want to be one, what do you do? Jeff Raz has drawn on his life's work to write a pair of narratives — one following a professional clown joining a huge show, and one following a clown student who just wants a job in a circus. It turns out the calling involves a lot of work, and, no surprise, it has mundane and spiritual sides that intertwine. The questions don't all get answered — how could they? — but the oldest craft in the world gets examined, with just the right amount of historical sidebar. It's a good book, and if you're curious about the clowning profession, you'll turn these pages."

 —**Bill Irwin,** *Sesame Street's Mr. Noodle,*
  MacArthur "Genius" and Tony Award winner

THE SECRET LIFE OF CLOWNS

A backstage tour of
Cirque du Soleil and
The Clown Conservatory

The Secret Life of Clowns can be purchased at www.secretlifeofclowns.com.

First Edition

Designed by Tracy Cox/Codex
www.itscodex.com

ISBN 978-0-9979048-1-9

This book is dedicated to the memories of Peggy Ford, Paoli Lacy, Joan Mankin, Caroline Jones and Juan Cárdenas, five people who helped create and grow The Clown Conservatory.

INTRODUCTION

IF YOU ARE A LOVER OF CIRCUS IN GENERAL or a fan of Cirque du Soleil or a clown aficionado, here is a peek at what happens behind the big top. If you are an actor, dancer, street performer, juggler, acrobat or aerialist, this book will spill some secrets from the allied art of clowning. If you are a clown, a clown student or a clown teacher, welcome to a master class from one of the most successful clown schools in America and a close-up view of the biggest circus organization on earth.

The Secret Life of Clowns is fiction created from the decade that I spent directing The Clown Conservatory in San Francisco. Over 70 percent of the students who graduated between 2000 and 2010 have had, and many continue to have, successful careers in circus and theater. They've been performing with Cirque du Soleil and Ringling Bros. and Barnum & Bailey, touring with *Stomp* and Broadway shows, guesting on *The Tonight Show*, founding a comedy club in Dubai, starring on the burlesque circuit with clown stripteases, working in hospitals with the Clown Care Unit and the Medical Clown Project, acting in Shakespeare productions and devising original plays, among many other impressive efforts.

I have long wanted to share the methods we developed at The Clown Conservatory. This book contains many of the ideas and exercises we used to teach professional clowns. But most clowning is learned live; it is an art of the body and of people playing together. You will notice that I give only a taste of what happened in most of the classes at The Clown Conservatory — mime and dance, circus skills and acrobatics, body awareness, improvisation, music and physical theater. A lot of the work we did in the core clowning class is missing as well. My hope is that by writing about the elements of clowning that sit comfortably on the page, I can give clowns and other artists, along with their fans, a peek at a methodology that nurtured a cadre of wonderful, versatile performers in San Francisco at the turn of the 21st century.

Fans of Konstantin Stanislavski's brilliant trio of books on acting (*An Actor Prepares*, *Building a Character* and *Creating a Role*) will quickly recognize the debt I owe this great Russian stage director, teacher and author; I borrowed his use of a fictional student to tell the story of a year in school. The other students and teachers in this book, and even the director, are also products of my imagination, although some people will recognize character traits or specific incidents — Bronkar Lee really did dance in front of San Francisco General Hospital accompanied by Luz Gaxiola on accordion, Jamarr Woodruff had a visceral reaction to putting whiteface makeup on his brown skin and wrote eloquently about it, and Fleur Alexander partnered with Natalie Pasquale to perform a clown routine with a smoking bong.

This student's-eye view of The Clown Conservatory makes up about half of the book. The other half comes from my 500-performance tour in the starring role of Cirque du Soleil's *Corteo*. While on the road, I continued to direct The Clown Conservatory from a laptop in my hotel room while the rest of the faculty ran the school back in San Francisco. From the moment I arrived in Montreal to prepare for the *Corteo* role, I tried to be my own best student, to follow the advice I gave my students. The Cirque du Soleil chapters are a fictionalized account of this tour, with many glimpses into the reality of backstage life at Cirque du Soleil.

These two points of view — a young student struggling to become a professional clown and his teacher performing in front of thousands of people every day — gives a complex picture of a profession that is often reduced to a punch line or a cliché. Along the way, you will get to hang out backstage at Cirque du Soleil, see performances close up and hear about some of the things that go awry under the big top. In addition, you'll find a series of brief profiles that spotlight some real Clown Conservatory alumni and mentors of mine.

Fiction can bring a deeper truth. Many years ago I wrote a play with Jael Weisman based on a trip I had taken to Europe. We sent blank cassette tapes and a list of questions to about a dozen folks I had traveled or stayed with, including a girlfriend I broke up with in

Paris. We transcribed the tapes and used their words to tell most of the story. When this ex-girlfriend saw the play, she was furious. I was shocked since we had only used her words, not mine, but she claimed the scene in Paris was all my side of the story. She was right, of course. When we re-wrote *Father-Land*, it was a fictional play that got much closer to the truth as I saw it (and it didn't include the Paris interlude).

The Secret Life of Clowns is my truth about training professional clowns and touring with Cirque du Soleil.

Jeff Raz
Alameda, CA May, 2016

CHAPTER ONE

"HI, MY NAME IS…"
The Clown Conservatory

"YOU ARE ALL STRANGE, ODD AND QUIRKY."

The Director, a large man with shoulder-length salt-and-pepper hair and an easy smile, stands in front of the class. He's wearing well-used black sweatpants, a long-sleeved black tee and a vest with the yellow sunburst logo of Cirque du Soleil embroidered on it.

"Everybody is strange but most people work hard to hide it. They have to."

I think about my playful dad, a professor who wears a blue suit and a boring tie to work every day.

"We clowns make a living off of our oddness. Here's how I see it: Imagine this is you with all your flaws and defects, mental and physical."

He points to himself as he slumps, looking slightly defective. "First, you have to step out of yourself…"

He steps sideways to his left, "…and train yourself to be skillful, with a clean line and a focused mind."

He is now straight and poised like a dancer. I see the acrobat he was a decade ago, before he started this school.

"Then, after you are trained up, you step back into your strangeness." He steps to his right and his big body is full of slight angles, his face open and warm, his eyes twinkling. He's a clown.

"But now you are a pro. You control your quirks, use them to make acts that will move people to laugh, move people to cry and…" He straightens up and pitches his voice an octave lower, "…move people to pay you."

My classmates and I laugh lightly. I am relieved to hear the Director begin by talking about paid work. I'm here at The Clown Conservatory because I want to get a job with a circus. I'm already a professional juggler, at least a professional street juggler, but I want to work in a circus. I arrived thinking that any gig will do, at least at first, but now, staring at the Cirque du Soleil logo on the Director's vest, I let myself dream big. The Director works for Cirque du Soleil, splitting his time between teaching and performing. He's here this afternoon but tonight he'll take a red-eye to Montreal. I'd love to be on that plane.

The Director jumps off the stage and runs to the back of the old high-school theater where we hold class. We swivel around to look at him.

"Let's start with something basic, the very simplest performance — one human being standing in front of a group of other humans, what we call an audience." He opens his arms in a broad gesture that includes the entire theater and all of us, sitting cross-legged in a semicircle on the floor.

"What happens between a person and an audience? Can you stand on stage with no unicycles, no dance moves, no card tricks, no gags borrowed from Chaplin or Keaton? Nothing. Just you and the audience."

The Director pauses. I try to imagine doing one of my street shows without my juggling equipment. What the hell would I do?

"Will you bore them? Do you deserve their attention?"

Of course I will bore them. I'm a good juggler but I need something to juggle.

"Who wants to go first?"

Roger, a tall guy in his late twenties with long black hair, an off-white ruffle-front tux shirt and designer track pants, jumps up. Roger has already made sure everyone knows he's a professional magician. He claims he's here just to add a little personality to his routine and he's not really into being a clown. He spins his black bowler hat to me, salutes the Director and says, "I'm your man!" The rest of us settle in to watch.

"Thank you for volunteering, Roger. Ronni, would you mind setting one of those blue tumbling mats on end to create a makeshift curtain?"

I met Ronni on the streetcar going to school on the first day, a short woman with purple hair and muscly arms carrying a backpack full of juggling clubs. We talked about the mathematics of juggling, my physics degree and her love for the Three Stooges. Now we juggle together whenever we can. She's almost as good as me, technically, but she doesn't have any performance material.

I jump up to help Ronni but she's already flipping the tumbling mat on end so I sit back down. The Director says, "Roger, will you please stand behind the flat that Ronni's set up and, when I give you the signal, walk out here on stage. Come center and say, 'Hello, my name is Roger' and then walk back behind the flat. Just that. Simple."

Roger high-fives Ronni as she trots back to sit on the floor and steps behind the flat. "Roger," the Director says, "we're ready for you." Roger pops out stage right. He takes a bow, comes center stage, flips his hair. "Roger here, over and out!" He then does a scraggly cartwheel, lands on his feet in another pose and slides back behind the flat. Roger may be a jerk but he definitely knows how to perform.

The Director claps and says, "Thank you, Roger. Now, would you try it again but this time do less. Just walk out, come center and say, 'Hello, my name is Roger.' Then walk behind the flat. Nothing more."

Roger enters again, skips the hair flip and says, "Hello, my name is Rogerrrrr!" We laugh as he walks upstage and takes a drink from an imaginary glass, a move we just learned in mime class.

The Director walks over to Roger, "You are showing us a certain Roger, a showman Roger. That's OK but it's not as interesting, or original, as the real Roger with all your flaws." Roger looks confused and a bit angry. "Clowns need to be real and vulnerable, which starts with standing in front of a group of people and saying 'hello' as simply as possible. Do you want to try one more time?"

"No, someone else can suffer for a while." Roger holds out his hand for me to throw him back his hat. When I do, he flips it onto his head as he sits down.

Anita, in her ensemble of a black sleeveless leotard, pink tights and matching hand-knit ankle warmers, tries next. She glides to center stage and stands in a perfect ballet fifth position, right heel at a 90-degree angle to her left big toe. She calmly says her line in slightly accented, perfectly articulated English, then glides back upstage.

The Director says, "Thank you, Anita, you move beautifully. Roger offered us 'The Performer' and now you offered us a different mask, 'The Perfect Dancer.' Neither of you gave us even a peek at the real you. We'd love to see you, Anita. Just you."

"Let me try again," Anita says. She enters and, for a moment, her face looks entirely different. Her mouth relaxes into a slight frown, her eyes are sad. But before she gets to center stage, she snaps back to her Perfect Dancer mask and keeps it until she exits. The sad Anita is gone.

Before she comes back out, the Director jumps up and says, "Thank you, Anita. You shared a moment of yourself and we are very grateful."

There is no answer from behind the flat. We wait for a few moments and when Anita appears her eyes are red.

Turning to us, the Director says, "This is hard. This may be the hardest exercise you do all year, although you won't think so when you're holding three-minute handstands or trying to juggle five balls. All the skills you are learning are important — you will need that handstand and those juggling chops — but you can't become a great clown without sharing your heart. If the audience doesn't see your heart, and feel your heart, they can't fall in love with you."

Starlight, who is comforting Anita, whispers, "Un momento, caro" and walks up to the Director. Since she is the only one of us with zero stage experience and no circus skills, I think she might nail this exercise. But when she comes on stage, her cowboy boots peeking out from under a tie-dyed skirt, she is as guarded, in her own smiling way, as Roger or Anita.

"What was your name before you took Starlight?" the Director asks.

"Jane. But I am not Jane anymore — I have become Starlight." Her smile is dazzling.

"Fine. But you were Jane when you were a little girl, yes?"

"Yes."

"Could you just come out and say 'Hello, my name is Jane.'"

Starlight tries a couple of times. We see a few flashes of a shy, scared little girl but each time she stops before she says "Jane." Finally she stomps back to her seat. "That is not me! I am not Jane. Jane died 19 years ago and I'm glad she's gone!" Her jaw is jutted and her stare is hard.

"Thank you for trying, Starlight. I'm sorry it was..." The Director searches for a word, gives up and quietly watches as Anita hugs Starlight. The two friends huddle in the far corner of the theater, whispering in Spanish.

"We are looking for the darker parts of our hearts. It can be painful. Clowns sometimes talk about 'channeling your inner child,' which usually means being playful. For Starlight, this might be where some of her tragedy is, too. Perhaps for others of you as well."

He looks at Roger, who looks away.

"A teacher of mine, Carlo Mazzone-Clementi, used to say that great clowning is 51 percent comedy and 49 percent tragedy. Get too much comedy, and it may be funny but it won't move our hearts."

Clowning is supposed to be fun but students are crying and the Director is talking about the need for tragedy. I pull my sweatshirt a little tighter around my chest. The rest of my classmates go up, one at a time and, one at a time, they fail. We get glimpses, a moment when someone suddenly looks real and, always, a little sad. But everyone snaps back to their "public face" within seconds.

The Director looks at me. I am terrified but slowly walk on stage.

My palms itch for some juggling balls or scarves or clubs, anything I can use to do something in front of my classmates. I have nothing. I feel naked. As I stand behind the flat, my mind churns, "I have no business being in this school. I have no right to be on stage."

"We're ready when you're ready."

I seriously consider running out of the room. Instead, I step out from behind the flat, see the audience, my classmates, and freeze. Then slowly back off. I take a deep breath.

The Director coaxes me, "We just want to see you. Just simply you."

I enter in a fog, stumble downstage, stutter my name, walk offstage. There is genuine applause. I peek out. My classmates are smiling and few are wiping their eyes.

"Good, good. We saw a little of you. Do it again, just exactly like that. Just you and us right here in this room."

I walk out, the fog gathers but I chase it away. I am standing in front of my classmates, really seeing them, feeling my own breath in my lungs, meeting their eyes. I say, "Hello, my name is Jake."

Jake's Journal #1, September 12

The Big Ideas:
- *Simplicity means standing on stage without anything fake, no "public face"*
- *51% comedy with 49% tragedy = Great Clowning*

Why does this matter to me?
- *So I feel in my heart that I belong on stage.*
- *So I don't throw a lot of stuff into my acts because I'm afraid to be in front of an audience.*

Exercises:
- *Enter; come onto the stage; say, "Hello, my name is Jake" and exit. Nothing more, nothing less.*
- *Keep working on headstands.*
- *Fixed point in mime is cool. Gotta work on drinking an invisible glass of water.*
- *I don't love dance but I might love my dance teacher. Do those stretches for her.*

My Ah-ha moment:
- *Simplicity = fucking hard*

CHAPTER TWO

A CRUMPLED OLD SHOE
MONTREAL, QUEBEC

Cirque du Soleil

THE INTERNATIONAL HEADQUARTERS of Cirque du Soleil looks like a three block long steel-and-glass parking garage, all hard-edged and ultra-modern. In front of the main entrance, sitting on a squat cement slab, is a large bronze sculpture of a clown shoe, old and crumpled looking.

I procrastinate in front of the shoe statue, watching my breath hit the chilly Montreal air. I want to be home. I'm tired from years on the road and then fatherhood and running a school. Can I still thrill audiences? Teaching young clowns seems easier than trying to do what I teach on a big stage in front of thousands of people. Cirque du Soleil is the biggest circus organization in human history, beloved for its innovative acrobatics, amorphous music and perfect bodies. I am a middle-aged clown who has been out of the ring and running a clown school for nearly a decade, a little old and crumpled looking.

Of course going home isn't an option. Besides needing the money — the school doesn't pay very well — it would be too embarrassing. My friends have been treating me like a big star for months. I loved it at first but then I started to get a little paranoid, thinking that all the attention was going to jinx it, that Cirque would find someone else or one of my kids would get really sick or my mom would take a turn for the worse or... but here I am and I need to do this right.

I have given myself this year of touring, of trying to do what I teach every day, to decide if I should stay at The Clown Conservatory. If I can't make it with Cirque du Soleil, why should my students listen to me? On the other hand, if I kick ass in the lead role in this big show, why should I go back to teaching? Touring or teaching? Or neither? My family will get my paychecks and some reflected glory but I can't imagine that will make up for me not being home.

One more deep, chilly breath and it's time to go in. My eyes sting from the sleep I didn't get in the performers' dorm, a large building filled with young Eastern European acrobats who drink cases of Canadian beer all night and listen to jaw-rattling techno pop.

I walk into Cirque Headquarters, try out my kindergarten French on the receptionist and get hustled off to the wig department. Two bubbly young women, dressed as cowgirls complete with boots, tight jeans and little horseshoe necklaces, sit me down in a salon chair. Keeping up a steady stream of French, they cover my head and most of my face with plastic wrap and Scotch tape. It takes them the better part of an hour to mummify me from the neck up, leaving only two little nose holes for me to breathe. They add the finishing touches by drawing in my hairline and eyebrows with a felt tip marker and then carefully peel the whole thing off. The show I'm joining, *Corteo*, features the performers' real hair. No wigs on anyone. This whole mummy business is either a scheduling mistake or a precaution against sudden-onset baldness, a concern, I suppose, when you hire old clowns.

After signing a pile of papers, getting an impressively thorough physical examination and lunching on a chicken Caesar in the spotless cafeteria, I arrive at the costume department. A trim, preppy young man helps me stuff my body into a baby blue sleeveless leotard that is only a couple of sizes too small. He then hands me a white belt and headband with a cheerful "Et voilà!" I put them on and look in the mirror at a large, lumpy Richard Simmons lookalike.

I have never been svelte but I used to have the body of an acrobatic "porter," the guy who throws around the smaller "flyers" — big muscles with a little padding to round things out. Nearly a decade of teaching has added a little more round and a little less muscle.

For the next 45 minutes, my preppy young friend measures me in excruciating detail, calling out my metric height and width to his assistant in French. I'm happy not to understand. When we're done, the assistant neatly folds my street clothes over his arm and leads me down the hall to a workshop where two burly artisans make a plaster cast of my mid-section from thighs to belly button. They tell me that my custom-made flying harness will be delivered to the *Corteo* tent in time for my first rehearsal and warn me not to lose weight, which might cause it to slip off while I am in midair. I assure them that I will do my best.

A short, chiseled man in his early 40s comes in as I'm zipping up my pants. He introduces himself as the head rigger and, after a bone-crushing handshake, leads me to one of the expansive, well-equipped acrobatic studios that are scattered throughout the Cirque complex. The room is at least three stories high with lots of sunlight shining in on the trampolines, trapezes and ropes hanging from the ceiling.

The head rigger takes a rock-climbing harness off a rack on the wall and adjusts the webbing. "Step into this. It is temporary so you can fly now, before they finish making your personal one." The harness goes on something like a diaper and the head rigger takes his time making sure that every strap is in place and tight. I want to say that I would be happy to wait to fly until my personal harness is done but think better of it.

Once the harness is ready, the head rigger clips either side of a large metal U to the D rings that are sewn into the harness where a cowboy would carry his six-guns. The bottom part of the U is then attached to a 60-foot-long metal rope coming down from a pulley hung from the ceiling. The metal U turns upside down when the metal rope is tightened.

We're joined by a woman who is a few years younger and a few centimeters taller than the head rigger and just as chiseled. She smiles, crushes my hand and tells me that she's my acrobatic trainer for the day. She double-checks my harness, the D rings, the U and the rest of the rigging. All is fine. She asks if I am ready to "go to tension." I don't know what she means but I say, "Good to go," raise a thumb with American panache and quickly find myself a dangling few feet off the ground like a piñata. I give another thumbs up, my acrobatic trainer says, "Tres bien. Allonz-y!" and starts a winch that winds the metal rope onto a big wheel, hoisting me into the air.

Everyone is being so careful and solicitous that I feel much more comfortable than I thought I would. When I signed the contract with Cirque du Soleil, I lied about not being afraid of heights. But now, as the harness tightens around my inner thighs, I feel like a flyer. It is actually fun, if a little strange, going slowly up to 15 feet and slowly back down. On the ground, more pampering, "Is it pinching? Do your legs hurt? Was it too fast coming down?"

The next time they take me up to 20 feet, back down and then up to 30 feet, where I find myself at eye level with a third-floor boardroom. The room, which has large windows facing the studio, is full of men and women in suits sitting around a big table watching a PowerPoint. I wave, they wave back and I pretend to swim in the air. We all laugh and I start to descend back to the floor.

Veni, vidi, vici! I came, I saw, I conquered! The clown teacher from San Francisco flies in to bring joy to the workaday life of the Suits of Cirque. Score one for the crumpled shoe.

SPOTLIGHT:
Clowning in America

Horses were the stars of Western circus at the beginning, in London around 1770. This means that the first circus clowns were trick riders who could also get laughs. British circus clowns invaded America quickly and did well in this country. Dan Rice is the most famous home-grown clown in antebellum America, still using horses in his show but best known for his humorous comments on current events, topical songs and Shakespeare parodies.

American clowns were very talkative until John Ringling switched to a 10,000-seat tent with three rings. The story goes that, realizing verbal jokes could no longer be heard by the back rows, the circus owner ordered Clown Alley to perform only visual gags. Ringling's Clown Alley in the late 19th and early 20th century was huge, nearly 50 clowns, as compared to the dozen or so touring on each Ringling unit today. The clowns were part of "spec" (the big opening and closing numbers that included all human and animal performers), did "carpet clowning" (quick sight gags while standing on the carpet between the audience and the rings) as well as big clown production numbers with elaborate props such as the Clown Car and the Firemen Gag. These production numbers involved more clowns, and more chaos, than the European clown entrees of the same time. The makeup of the European White Clown (full whiteface with delicate black and red accents) and the Auguste (large white shapes around the eyes and mouth with black and red accents and a large red nose) did cross the Atlantic even if their particular personalities and carefully crafted entrees did not. Lou Jacobs, Bozo and others created a distinctly American hybrid by coupling a full white face with a huge red nose and wig.

In the 1930s, Otto Griebling and Emmett Kelly added a radically different look to the American circus — the Tramp clown. Dressed in rags with a white, downturned mouth in a sea of stubble, the Tramp clown's melancholy was in stark contrast to the sparkle and smiles of every other performer in the show. During the Ringling spec, with dozens of elephants and hundreds of acrobats, Griebling would sit on the ring curb slowly knitting. By the end of the spec, all eyes were on the tramp clown. Kelly's routine where he tries to sweep up a spotlight is the most famous Tramp Clown routine. The many imitators of Charlie Chaplin's "Little Tramp" in America's Clown Alleys looked and moved like the movie star and not with the slow sadness of Tramp Clowns.

The New Circus movement started in the mid-1970s in San Francisco. The Pickle Family Circus clowns — Larry Pisoni, Geoff Hoyle and Bill Irwin — created original entrees in the European style, even though their look was quite eclectic. Make*A*Circus offered free shows in Bay Area parks, with workshops and performances by the audience, anticipating what would later be called Social Circus. Cirque du Soleil, the largest and most famous New Circus, started in Quebec almost a decade later.

CHAPTER THREE

CLOWN SCHOOL, EARLY DAYS
The Clown Conservatory

OUR MIME TEACHER HAS FINALLY stopped talking and school is over for the week. I turn right outside of the main door, run up the stairs and through the parking lot of the neighboring apartment building to get to the N Judah stop. No train yet. I stare down Carl Street into the heart of the Haight-Ashbury and see only a few bike riders coming my way. It is a beautiful San Francisco autumn evening but I'm too worn out to enjoy it. My first few weeks at The Clown Conservatory have been exhausting. My body aches all over and I don't even know if I should be here.

All I want out of this year at clown school is enough training to get a job with a circus. This has been a dream of mine since I learned to juggle 10 years ago. My physics degree sounds fancy but I bought the books and paid my rent by busking, juggling on the streets of Boston. Physics isn't fun anymore; performing is.

But learning to be a professional clown is different than juggling on the streets and San Francisco is a tough city to live in. I'm paying way too much for a small room in a small apartment way out in the cold, foggy neighborhood called The Sunset, spending way too much time on public transportation and eating way too much rice and beans.

Last February, when I told my folks I had applied to a clown school 3,000 miles away, my dad smiled and said, "I went to school for 20 years, got a PhD and became a professor. Life in a circus might be more fun." I looked at my mother to see her jaw tighten. She sighed and said, "We'll talk about it if you get accepted."

On April 1, the same day I got a letter inviting me to join the U.C.

Berkeley Physics Graduate Program, an email arrived from The Clown Conservatory. I was in. My parents thought it was an April Fools' joke. When I convinced them it was real and that I wanted to study clowning in San Francisco and not physics across the Bay in Berkeley, my mother offered me a deal. "You can defer grad school for a year and go to clown school. If you are offered a circus contract by the time you graduate next summer, you take it. If not, you go Berkeley in the fall." Of course I said "OK." I'm not sure either of them believed I'd be able to get a circus job and they didn't offer to help pay for clown school, so I'm living off the money I made street performing over the summer.

I don't know if I want to spend my life performing but I have to try to get at least one tour with a circus. Any circus. That seemed pretty easy back when I was home in New Jersey but now, sitting on this small, fold-down bench at the streetcar stop in front of The Clown Conservatory, it seems a lot harder.

At 9:00 on our first day, without any welcoming speeches or orientation or getting-to-know-you games, we started our first class — acrobatics. By 9:05, my classmates and I were lying face down on worn-out blue tumbling mats on the floor of a repurposed, but not renovated, high school theater, stretching our ligaments beyond where ligaments should stretch. At 9:30 I was balancing on my head with our teacher, a former Chinese circus star, holding my feet and encouraging me to "Be strong!" I just wanted to live long enough to eat lunch.

The streetcar finally rumbles into sight, I grab my bag and hop up from the bench but the train is so packed with Friday commuters heading home from the Financial District that the driver doesn't even slow down. I scream. A woman on the sidewalk gives me a disgusted look, picks up her little boy and starts walking to the next stop. I flip down the bench and sit again. I take a deep breath.

Without thinking, I open my backpack and pull out my school journal. Four years of college taught me, "When the going gets tough, the tough study."

The first page is stained with dried sweat but I can make out some of my smudged notes.

> **"Acrobatics**...discipline, risk, partnership...great skills for any performer...Some students will learn to professional level... create clown acrobatics acts."

Thinking about my classmates and feeling my own aching body, I can't imagine any of us doing acrobatics at a professional level.

*"**Acrobatic training** = headstands, handstands, doubles, tumbling."*

A headstand seemed possible that first day, although doing one alone is still a ways off. Standing on my hands, however, is flat-out crazy. We tried handstands up against a wall this morning and I thought I was going to smash my face into the floor. "Doubles" is when someone stands on your shoulders or thighs or somewhere else, although we haven't gotten that far. Tumbling is like gymnastics — the rolls and cartwheels are OK but after that it gets dangerous. Flips are for the professional acrobatic students who train down the hall in the big gym. They are superhumans with really hot bodies. We clown students are a little dorky and definitely not hot.

I turn the page to my notes from Circus Skills class. On that first day, Ronni and I showed off some ball passing tricks, which impressed our classmates. On the other hand, Dan is a monster on his unicycle, which makes me more than a little jealous. We also balanced brooms all over our bodies and learned to ride a rolla-bolla, a wooden plank rolling back and forth on a metal cylinder.

Circus Skills is my sweet spot and I left that first class feeling good. Dance was next, which didn't thrill me, especially because the syllabus mentioned ballet. Ballet is the opposite of clowning — all fake movements and tensed muscles.

The first thing I noticed when I walked into the downstairs dance studio was that our dance teacher is beautiful. She is tall and lithe with dark curly hair and a sweet smile.

*"**Ballet** = physical language of circus. Must know basics of ballet to be in circus. Strength, Line, Organization of Ballet = great for clowns."*

I'm not sure about ballet being great for clowns — I can't imagine the old masters like Lou Jacobs and Emmett Kelly in tights and toe shoes. But when I looked at myself in the big mirror on the dance studio wall yesterday, my legs had a "cleaner line" and my arms were almost graceful. Maybe I can learn to dance a little, if only to impress our teacher.

I thought the mime class would be all about making invisible walls and pulling invisible ropes. And I thought there would be no talking in class. The teacher, a small, wiry woman in her early 50s, talks a lot.

> *"Mime = Clarity of Movement, Clarity of Purpose. Isolate a movement, Break it into parts, Explore Rhythm of different parts, then Play for different Dramatic effects."*

We did learn how to make an invisible wall, how to "isolate a movement," and it is a lot harder than it looks. I always thought that mimes were just jugglers who didn't have the discipline to practice.

> *"Mime = able to stand still. Stillness is Alive and Focused. Neutrality = state of Human-ness underneath our separate Personalities. Transcend the Ordinary = Higher Artistic plane that Includes, Inspires and Unifies everyone."*

Our mime teacher studied in France so she likes to go off about the "higher artistic plane" and "human-ness underneath our separate personalities." I'm pretty sure that most circus directors couldn't give a shit about any of that stuff. Even so, I can see how the silent-movie clowns, and even some old circus clowns, used a lot of mime.

The Body Awareness class, which we only have on Thursdays, is supposed to help us recover from our other classes. By the time we got to the first Body Awareness class, I would have loved a long nap or maybe a massage, a hot tub and a whisky sour.

No such luck.

We spent the whole first class focused on "attending," quietly noticing everything that was going in our "internal world" and then our "external world."

> *"Our bodies = both our life and our art. Body Awareness = navigating between the Internal World (thoughts, feelings) and External World (skills, tricks). Access to Internal World = feeling, sensitivity,*

vulnerability. Capable of creating deep human connections with your audience."

Strange as it was, an hour of attending felt pretty good after four days of clowning, acrobatics, dance, mime and circus skills. I'm still a little confused about how my internal world is important for clowning. I've been all about throwing things and jokes and passing the hat. If that exercise where we had to come out and just say our name is any indication, the internal world may be harder to learn than the external.

I look up from my notebook to see another N Judah streetcar coming over the hill. Blessedly, it stops. I shove my notebook into my backpack, step on the train and try to find a little wiggle room in the crush of rush-hour commuters escaping their offices downtown. There is a sliver of space near the back door between a couple of middle-aged Suits and I wedge myself in. Staring out the long, thin window in the folding back door, looking out at the fog belt of San Francisco, I think about this idea of the internal world and the external world.

Jake's Journal #2, September 24

The Big Questions:
- What do I really need to get a job in a circus? What does it take to be a pro?

Why do my classes matter to me?
- We have our first show in less than a month and I don't want to suck.
- This whole internal/external thing is a little too woo-woo for a guy from New Jersey but I do want audiences to love me, not just admire my juggling.
- The discipline of acrobatics is good for clowns. The risks you take doing acrobatics, even the kind of baby acro we do, can make you braver on stage.
- Mimes, after all the jokes, know how to be eloquent with their bodies.

Homework: The 5 'R's
- **R**ehearsal — class assignments + acts for the show
- **R**eading — assigned reading every week + meeting with my "book club" (Starlight, who I like pretty much and Bari, who is Ronni's roommate.)
- T**R**aining — 1 or 2 hours/day outside of class working on circus skills, acro, dance, mime and music (no music yet but we hear it's coming.)
- W**R**iting — keep a journal.
- **R**esearch — we need to research and write a short paper about a clown culture or practice from another part of the world or a clown about whom very little has been published. Not exactly a physics paper (thank god).

Exercises:
- Work on handstands. Try not to kill myself.
- Learn the steps for the group dance number.
- Juggle with Ronni.
- Try doing nothing sometimes when I feel exhausted instead of drinking another cup of tea.

My Ah-ha moment:
- Clown school is not as fun as I thought it would be; it might be as much work as grad school.

CHAPTER FOUR

A DEAD CLOWN
WASHINGTON, D.C.

Cirque du Soleil

THE SHUTTLE TURNS OUT OF THE AIRPORT and onto the high-way heading toward the nation's capital where *Corteo* is just finishing up a two-month run. As we hit a snarl of traffic, I take a deep breath and struggle to calm my nerves. The Cirque du Soleil folks wanted me to fly in yesterday but I needed to teach so I took the red-eye. My plane was late and my first rehearsal with the touring troupe starts in under an hour. Another deep breath.

I look around at the other passengers. They are all plugged in — one guy is watching his mini TV, one is doing email on his Blackberry while making dinner reservations on his cell and the rest of the passengers are listening to their iPods. The driver is on his phone and reading a map on his laptop. They are all off in their own worlds.

Artists need to see and hear what is around us — the faint lilt of the radio, the sirens, the blue of the police lights, the oranges and reds of the leaves, the unique style of driving that is part of every city. We need to, as the old saying goes, be here now. We then need to notice what happens inside ourselves, how we feel and think, especially when we are uncomfortable. I am in a van in a city I don't know with seven strange men and the only reason I feel comfortable is that I paid $26 and it says "Super Shuttle" on the side.

Artists need to avoid reaching for something entertaining when we are bored or nervous. This is not romantic. It means a lot of looking out of windows, feeling lonely in order to experience the world rather than experiencing the digested experiences of others. This is an es-sential skill for clowns, the ability to calm our insides so we can stay connected with the world around us, whether it is seven men in a van or an audience in a circus tent or a class full of students.

A few blocks from the Capitol, I see the top of a huge yellow-and-blue striped tent peeking out between the office buildings. I smile as my jaded old clown soul melts a little. This is cool.

The van stops, I open the sliding door and jump out, dragging my rollie behind me. I only have a few minutes to change into sweats before walking on stage to rehearse the flying scene.

A wiry man with curly black hair and a hard-to-place accent helps me into my new, custom-made harness. As he adjusts the straps that go between my legs, he tells me his name is Pascal, the Head Rigger, and adds, "If you die, it is my fault." He takes a metal U, a smaller version of the one I used in Montreal, and attaches one end to a single line of metal rope and the other ends to the D rings on my harness. There are little angel wings attached to the metal rope. I am an Angel Clown.

The riggers take me to tension, I give the thumbs up and I fly to the top of the tent. Right away it's bad — the new harness pulls in my groin and my whole body tips forward at a strange angle. My stomach churns. I try to remember how good flying felt in Montreal but I end up making a strange noise and they bring me down quickly. Pascal says, "You don't want to hang too long in a harness, you know, because the carbon dioxide can build up in your legs and when we take you down, it will release, go straight to your heart and…" He runs his finger across his throat. A Dead Clown.

I take off the harness and give it to two riggers to adjust while Pascal takes me over to an ornate metal-framed bed. "Let's try the flying bed. It will be better for you." He pulls a short safety line through a slit in the sheets as the riggers help me back into my harness. I straddle the bed, clip the safety line to a D ring and grab the headboard.

"Going to tension." The bed wiggles under me, the same feeling you get from a late-night 5.0 earthquake. I look up to where the wires that are attached to the four corners of the bed disappear into a metal track near the top of the tent. The track arcs across to the other side of the stage. Pascal tells me that they are going to take me up to 10 meters, slowly, and then fly the bed across the stage, slowly, and land it back down on the other side, gently.

"Since this is your first time, we will not stop the bed in the middle and try to throw you off. We want to keep you alive, at least for now."

In the show, Antonio, the current Dead Clown, gets good laughs when the bed tips forward and then, when it tips the other way, by rolling backward with his feet in the air.

A moment later, the bed and I fly up and then glide toward the far side of the tent. Watching someone else ride a floating bed is a whole lot more fun than riding a floating bed. This is worse than flying without the bed — I miss the pull of the wires on my harness and flinch every time the bed jiggles under my butt. The bed stops. We are at the apex of the track, high above center stage. I sit for a minute, trying to breathe normally and slow my heart rate down.

I sit some more.

And sit.

I finally give a thumbs up and say, "Good to go. I'm ready to come down."

There is some discussion in French 30 feet below me.

I sit.

I sweat.

Finally, Pascal calls up to me, "The computer, it is stubborn. It will not let the bed come down without trying to throw you off first." Sweat pops off my face like a character in the comics. "No worry, Dead Clown, we will be gentle. This is your first time, non?"

I grab the bed frame and white-knuckle it through the impossibly slow forward tip. Then I roll onto my back as the bed tips the other way and I start to panic. My scrambled brain decides that speaking in French will save me. I try to put together a sentence that will tell Pascal I will give him whatever he wants if they will only bring me down. "J'appelle mort!" is all that comes out. Laughter floats up. "And my name is Pascal. Nice to meet you, Dead."

Finally, the bed is flat again and we are heading down into the wings offstage. My clothes are soaked.

My next two days are bad. I spend hours in my hotel room trying to figure out how to get out of my contract — I'll do anything to get back to my school and away from that flying bed. During the shows, I dress all in black and follow Antonio everywhere except onto the stage. Everyone ignores me or pushes me out of the way because I'm always blocking someone's entrance. Everyone loves Antonio. He has a backstage routine that includes dozens of cheek kisses with beautiful aerialists, hugs with the hunky acrobats, handshakes with the riggers and little jokes and pranks here and there. I begin to hate Antonio.

I work hard to change my attitude:

> "Nearly everyone in the cast flies at some point. Flying is one of the safest things in the show — the Planche acrobats do double summersaults with double twists, landing on a two-foot-square piece of wood."
> "Flying is a metaphor and I need to embrace it."
> "Antonio is an actor, not an acrobat. He flies 10 times a week without breaking a sweat. Embrace my inner Antonio."

It's day three and I'm still panicked. On my way to catch the train from the hotel to the tent, I take a shortcut through a swanky hotel lobby packed with men in blue suits and boring ties. I overhear a conversation about the convention's keynote speaker and it hits me:

> "Here's my choice: Learn to fly or become a Suit."

We performers are special — we get to do things that these conventioneers can't even dream of. But it is impossible to feel special all the time. Mostly, we think about our fears and our day-to-day problems and try to get comfortable, just like everyone else. We couldn't make it through the day if we lived in the awe and splendor all the time. But it helps to think about the gifts we are given occasionally.

After a quick train ride I'm rehearsing the final scene, flying across the stage at 30 feet on a bicycle, smiling the whole way. The pull of the ropes on my harness and the sight of the safety lines coming off the handlebars make me very happy. I land the bike, unclip and dismount. Two riggers clip the wire rope with angel wings onto my harness and take me to 30 feet. Up and down a couple of times and then I'm flying through a hole near the tent's peak where the Assistant Head Rigger, Freddo, pulls me to a platform and safety. I'm still smiling when I get back down the ladders attached to the support truss and onto terra firma. Right on to the flying bed, trying to keep my mood up and my heart rate down. It's not fun, yet, but I make it across and when the bed touches down on the far side of the tent, I unclip and high-five everyone in sight.

I run into the Artistic Tent, the scaled-down version of the Big Top where we dress and warm up, crowing about my feat of flying and my defeat of fear. A few dozen former Olympic athletes stare at me. I feel like a boy bragging to a bunch of BMX pros that he just ditched his training wheels.

It's not cool to be so excited.

I slink over to my dressing table and look in the mirror. I'm still smiling. I think of my students, how I ask them to be vulnerable and even tell them that there is power in vulnerability. They look at the acrobats training in the gym down the hall and see perfection. Then they look at themselves and feel weak and silly. I have to convince them that the audience might admire the perfection of an acrobat but they will fall in love with the deeply flawed humanity of a clown. This is easier to teach than to do. For the moment, though, I can relax. Tonight I'll watch the show again and, in the morning, fly home for a short stint of teaching before I start performing.

SPOTLIGHT:
Patty Gallagher

Patty already had a PhD in theater when she joined the first class at The Clown Conservatory. She had also trained extensively in Bali and performed, in Spanish, with a theater company in Quito, Ecuador. After she graduated, Patty introduced the idea of creating a Clown Conservatory syllabus, which was the first step in turning some good ideas about clowning into a methodology for training professionals.

For years, Patty came back to The Clown Conservatory to teach workshops, often on Balinese dance. She would stand right behind a student and move their arms with her arms, their legs with her legs, almost like a puppeteer. She explained that this is the way her Balinese teacher taught her, the way this art form was passed on. Far from feeling manipulated, the students thrilled at the physical connection, the rigor and the love Patty poured into them.

Patty is now a tenured professor at the University of California Santa Cruz, training many young clowns and actors. And she continues to act around the U.S. and in Ecuador and India. Her tour-de-force as Winnie in Samuel Beckett's *Happy Days,* a role that demands physical acting skill but takes away most of an actor's physical tools, still stands out as one of my favorite moments in a theater.

"Buried first up to her waist, and later up to her neck, in a gargantuan mound of earth, the relentless optimist prattles on in the face of doom...Nothing happens (very, very slowly) and yet everything hangs in the balance...Gallagher is nothing short of marvelous in one of the most demanding parts in the Beckett canon."

—Karen D'Souza for the
San Jose Mercury News

CHAPTER FIVE

SHOWTIME!

The Clown Conservatory

"WELCOME. THANK YOU FOR COMING. We have nothing to offer you."

Our Director, who got back from his final training with Cirque du Soleil in D.C. last week, is addressing the audience sitting on folding chairs in our classroom. He's sporting a button-down blue shirt and gray slacks with his Cirque du Soleil vest. "Flying colors" he calls it. My classmates and I are in our cleanest workout clothes, nervously waiting in the improvised wings. The audience is sitting on what once was the stage of our old high school theater and we're performing on blue mats covering the floor. We need the extra room for our acrobatics act and the big dance number.

It's week five and we're already doing a public show. Peeking out, I'm relieved to see that our "public" is made up mainly of a few friends, some of our instructors and the sinuous, well-tattooed acrobatic students. The Director is right that we have nothing to offer, but I can't believe he'd say it.

"Although we have nothing to offer you, you have a lot to offer us. We need you to play with us. Clowns have to play with audiences; that is the most important thing we do. We also play with each other, with our props and costumes and with our own hearts, minds and bodies. Clowning is all about playing with partners."

This idea of partnership has been a main theme in Core Clowning class lately. All week we have been showing the Director routines we created in our other classes and he's been pushing us to be better partners. In Circus Skills class, Ronni and I put together a simple duet ball-juggling act — first a few solo three-ball tricks in sync, then passing six balls while still both facing the audience and finally turning to pass seven balls facing each other. I thought it went pretty well when we showed it to the Director.

"Jake and Ronni, you are completely focused on the juggling, which is fine for a juggling act. For it to become a clown act, you also have to find a relationship between the two of you, two clowns, a clown partnership."

Every lunch this week, Ronni and I got together to rehearse our act. We tried to find the clown partnership by singing a song during the act, then by adding knock-knock jokes and finally trying to do some doubles acrobatics, a thigh stand, while we juggled. Mainly, we dropped a lot.

Virginie, who spent a year at a circus school in her native France, showed the Director a club-juggling act that had more angst than skill and ended with her throwing the clubs offstage.

"Your juggling clubs are partners too, Virginie. If you were working with Ronni, say, instead of the clubs, would you throw her offstage? That might be a bit disrespectful. A partnership with an inanimate object seems a little strange, I know. Try imagining your clubs as human partners and treat them accordingly."

Dan, who grew up in Atlanta watching UniverSoul Circus and then performed with the summer camp at Circus Smirkus in Vermont, did some nice unicycle tricks and seemed to treat his one-wheeled partner with a lot of respect.

"You did a nice job with your unicycle. Now you also need to partner with yourself, which is what is sometimes called character. You partner with your mind when you structure the act and you partner with your body when you find your unique way of moving with your unicycle. Add in your heart, including the darker corners of your heart, and you have a strong partnership with yourself. Your head, your body and your heart."

The Director says, "Ladies and Gentlemen, welcome to the very first performance of the students of The Clown Conservatory!"

The next 45 minutes are a blur to me. Backstage after the final bow, I remember that Ronni and I had dropped a few balls and, in the acrobatics act, my handstand, which is now one of the best in the class, wasn't. That final dance number seemed a bit different than when we rehearsed yesterday and I don't remember the mime scene at all, which might be for the best.

After the audience has said their "Good shows" and filed out, the Director asks us to stand in a circle in the middle of the mats. "Would each of you tell us of one moment from that show that really worked." Ronni shrugs and says, "We fucked up — there were juggling balls everywhere but in our hands." She gives me a limp grin and another shrug.

The Director smiles and says, "OK, but what worked? Let's start there."

Dan chimes in, "Ronni caught that final ball right on cue, even though she wasn't actually juggling by then." Dan always tries to make folks feel better, even if it comes out sideways sometimes. Ronni mouths, "Thank you, Dan" as the Director continues.

"O.K. That is something that worked for Ronni. How about something that you did that worked, Dan."

Dan says, "I nailed a new trick," which is true — he walked his feet on the tire of the unicycle and it got a big reaction. Virginie thinks throwing her juggling clubs at the audience, something she hadn't done in rehearsal, was a great addition, "Really freaked them out." Anita says we were all together for the first few bars of the dance number, "Well, maybe just the first bar" and Starlight feels supported by the rest of us even if she was only handing out props.

When my turn comes, I have to admit I don't remember much from the show. The Director asks, "What happened, Jake? Why don't you remember?"

"I don't know; it's mostly a blur."

Looking around, he asks, "Did anyone else find themselves in a blur during the show?"

A few of my classmates sheepishly nod their heads. Bari, a bartender turned street musician who shares an apartment with Ronni, says she doesn't remember anything of the show. "I always just black out on stage." I'm amazed since she often brags about street performing across Europe. Her skinny body, which usually looks strong and tough, looks frail and awkward.

The Director says, "This happens to a lot of people. It's a healthy brain's way of coping with stress." Bari looks at me with a smile, crosses her eyes and says, "Healthy brain? I don't think so." The Director laughs, "Oh, yes, you have healthy brains. You just need to convince them to find other ways of coping with stress and, even better, lowering your stress level when you are on stage. Clowns need to stay completely aware on stage. Clowns have to be the opposite of blacked out — we have to be supernaturally tuned in."

Roger says, "No disrespect, Bari, Jake," and gives us each a closed-lip smile, "but I was totally tuned in to the audience. You gotta be to do good magic. My card tricks went over well, like they always do." He tilts his head, smiles and shrugs.

The Director nods, "You are right, Roger, the audience applauded for your tricks and you were tuned in to their applause. But you didn't partner with Starlight, who was handing you your props. You tend to play straight ahead to the audience while ignoring your performing partner. Part of clowning is letting yourself be interested sideways as well as straight ahead."

Anita steps forward and speaks slowly and louder than usual, "It is not fair for you to judge us for this show. Back in Mexico City, we spent a whole year preparing for our first dance recital. For this show, here in San Francisco, we rehearsed for one week. One week and you expect us to be tuned in? This is not possible."

There were a lot of nods and Starlight mumbles, "Amen, mi hermana."

"You are right, Anita," the Director says, "I put you in an impossible situation. You were out there trying to remember new choreography, perform half-learned acrobatics tricks, sharing a stage with people you barely know and, as if that wasn't enough, I'm demanding that you partner with the audience. This is not fair." He gives Anita a smile and she looks away. The Director turns to us and adds, "But it is necessary. The real art of clowning happens in the space between the audience and the stage. It is different from any other art form in that way. You need to have audiences early and often to learn the art of connecting with the people. You need to learn to love the people who buy our tickets and sit in our seats."

The room gets quiet.

"You all did a good job today. The show was put together with odds and ends from your different classes like a sculpture made from the contents of a recycling bin. It was not a Rodin." Virginie snorts and the Director continues, "We needed material — some juggling acts, dances, sleight of hand, unicycle rides — as an excuse to get you in front of the audience. You'll learn routines soon and start making better material. Our clown grandparents left us lots of great material and it is yours for the taking. But today our focus wasn't on routines, it was on the relationship with the audience. We used the external, the routines, as a way to explore the internal, how you can be tuned in to everything at once on stage."

With a wave of his arm, the Director ends the discussion, "A very good first show and an even better debrief. See you all Monday morning when we'll start working on show number two!"

After hugs all around and a few half-hearted "Good jobs," I run up the hill and right onto the waiting streetcar. Ronni slides between the closing doors behind me and, miraculously, there are two empty seats across from the back door. We quietly sit there for a few minutes, squished together between the window and a large man who is practically sitting on Ronni. The guy gets off and Ronni says, "We should have just focused on the juggling and screw the relationship. That show was embarrassing."

"Yeah. Sorry. I was really off."

"Don't go all hangdog on me. It was both of us. Juggling is like math…hell, juggling is math, height equals time and all that. Juggling is hard science and we got too soft trying to do that relationship stuff."

"Yeah. Maybe. The acro was kinda fun, you know, even if it fucked us up in the show."

"You just like grabbing my thighs."

"What? I don't…I mean…it's acrobatics…"

"Relax, Jake, whoa. I'm just fucking with you. I know we're cool."

"Yeah. Sorry. We're cool."

We sit quietly as the train rolls west. I like Ronni a lot; she's my only friend here, and maybe I do enjoy holding her when we do acrobatics — but I wasn't trying to feel her up. We're performing partners; why did she have to go and make things weird between us?

"This is me. See you Monday."

Ronni gives me a kiss on the cheek and gets off the streetcar. I watch her swing her backpack over her shoulder as she walks away. I've still got a mile or so to go. An old man in a tweed suit sits down next to me and opens a book.

Maybe she was dropping a hint with her joke about grabbing her thighs. Maybe she wants a relationship. I always miss those kinds of things. But I don't know if it's worth getting all romantic…if she really does want to get romantic. Maybe she was just making a joke. If I make the wrong move, I could mess up everything…

Jake's Journal #3, October 20

The Big Idea:
- *Clowning is about relationships.*

Why does it matter to me?
- *To learn to be completely awake on stage so I can be more than a juggling dude.*
- *If our clown grandparents left us wonderful clown acts, why am I always trying to create new routines?*
- *I won a handstand contest, 42 seconds (against the wall). In your face!*

Exercises:
- *Perform a lot and don't black out.*
- *Keep juggling with Ronni but don't touch her thighs. Or do touch her thighs but not while we're juggling.*
- *Work on my dance steps WITH the music; if your dance steps don't happen at the right part of the music, the audience doesn't applaud and, worse, the dance teacher doesn't hug you and say, "good job."*
- *Neutral Mask (mime class) – looked so easy: just put on a mask without any expression and act with my body. But showing emotions without my face was almost impossible.*

My Ah-ha moment:
- *I'm not the only one who blacks out on stage.*

CHAPTER SIX

GOLDEN MISTAKES
The Clown Conservatory

...THE STREETCAR STOPS, the old man closes his book and gets off. I realize we're already past my apartment and the train is moving again so I wait to hop out at the next stop. The warm San Francisco evening has a salty bite out here near the ocean and I remember I need to get food for my roommates and me.

In a corner store, I mindlessly juggle three oranges. A young boy sees me and freezes. I juggle for him, he hides behind his dad's leg and I stop. As I put the oranges down, the dad says, "Hey, that was good. Know any tricks?" I pick up the oranges again and do a few moves from my juggling act. The little boy slowly comes out of his hiding place. I try a 360-degree turn in the narrow aisle and drop an orange.

"Sorry," I say, "it's cramped in here." I'm embarrassed for missing an easy trick. The boy smiles and picks up the orange. He throws it to me, I catch it in the juggling pattern and he hops up and down, laughing. He holds out his hands and I soft-toss him another orange. He drops it, laughs, picks it up and throws it back for me to juggle. He screams with delight. We throw back and forth, the boy dropping every throw and me juggling.

After a while, I catch the orange and, instead of throwing it back to the boy, I do a few fancy three-ball moves. The dad is beaming, the storekeeper is giving me a big thumbs up from behind the register and the other four or five customers are staring at me. Another 360-degree turn; this time I catch the orange with a flourish, and everyone claps.

I give the boy one orange, take a bow and, thrilled but a little embarrassed, take my basket to the checkout. The storekeeper gives me the other two oranges and, as I'm leaving, the dad yells, "Thank you. You made our day." The boy is trying to juggle his orange as I turn the corner to home.

The applause I got in the store was louder than the applause Ronni and I got in the show. All I did was juggle three oranges. My memory of the show in the corner store is clear, not a blur like the school show. Why am I even in school? I should be hanging out at corner stores juggling with kids and getting free food.

The applause for my street shows, if I am honest with myself, is more like the applause Ronni and I got than the applause in the store. What is different? In the store, I didn't have my costume or my equipment and I didn't use my patter. It was just me and a little boy who wanted to play and didn't care if the oranges hit the ground. In fact, the act didn't get good until I dropped that orange. That was when the boy started playing with me.

On Monday morning, the streetcar is already crowded so I grab a strap and stand near the front of the car. As we get near Ronni's stop, I want her to get on and I don't want her to get on. She gets on, gives me a big hug and starts chattering about her weekend working in a scene shop. Ronni took theater tech in high school and her carpentry skills are paying off for her now. She's excited about the set she's building and I'm happy to stand close to her and listen. Maybe we're good.

Class doesn't start for a few minutes so Ronni stays on one stop past the school to go get a coffee. I run down the stairs to catch the Director before he gets busy. He's in the old theater so I get to brag about my little show, how I was simply myself and how clear it was in my memory. I leave out the part about dropping the orange.

"Congratulations, Jake. Nice work." The Director puts a big arm over my shoulder and signals for the rest of the class to sit down. Ronni pushes the door open with her butt and comes in holding two big cups. The Director says, "Jake used a lot of our themes from last week to do something special in the produce section of a bodega." He turns to me. "You were simply yourself, without your patter or costume or equipment to hide behind. And you partnered with the oranges, with the boy, who was your clown partner for the moment, and then with your audience." He turns to the class, "Give Jake a hand."

I take a bow and see my classmates looking at me with a satisfying combination of respect and jealousy. I sneak a wink at Ronni, who winks back and hands me a cup of hot tea. I could love this woman.

"All clowns should look for moments to practice outside of class, especially with children. Children give immediate feedback. They can teach you more in a few minutes than I can in a week, as Jake's story attests." I start to sit down but the Director stops me with, "Before we move on to the lesson for today, I have a question for you, Jake. You said the boy threw oranges back and forth with you, right?"

"Yes. We juggled, in a way."

"How did the boy get the first orange to throw to you?"

I admit I dropped that first orange and the Director gives a little hop, claps his hands a few times and turns to the class, "Great! Perfect! A golden mistake! Thank you, Jake, you are the teacher today." He signals me to stand in his spot.

My face gets red as my classmates give me a nervous round of applause. I stand there for a moment and, unable to think of anything to say, take another awkward bow.

The Director say, "I'm not teasing you, Jake. You did a wonderful thing in your bodega show — you made a golden mistake. When you dropped that first orange, you created a connection with the boy. The boy sees an orange coming and he is thrilled. He thinks 'My turn to play!' and throws it back to you, which was the start of something beautiful."

The Director is happy that I messed up a 360-degree turn with three oranges, an amateur mistake. He gestures for me to join with the class. I quickly sit down next to Starlight, who gives me a hug and whispers, "Nice work, Jake-o."

The Director starts pacing. "That drop wasn't a mistake, a moment when you were less than perfect, a chink in the armor of a professional juggler. Not at all! That drop gave you the chance to connect with the boy. That was a moment for great clowning, a golden mistake.

"Clowns live or die by golden mistakes. But in order to make your mistakes golden, you have to be completely aware on stage, like Jake was when the boy picked up the orange. And you have to have the skills to make the gold, like when Jake integrated the boy's throw into his juggling pattern. Finally, you have to know how to partner with everyone around you, like Jake did, almost accidentally, with the whole store."

Ronni raises her hand and, without waiting to be called on, says, "Clowns may love mistakes but jugglers don't. We can't survive very long if our balls are on the ground." A few of the non-jugglers laugh at Ronni's hackneyed ball joke. I groan. Ronni shoots me a look and stands up to face the Director, "Seriously, with juggling and acrobatics and a lot of other circus skills, you pay for your mistakes. Big time. You've got to try to be perfect."

The Director says, "Yes, yes! Ronni, you are right about jugglers and acrobats…and clowns. We've got to try to be perfect!" "What?" Ronni says, "You were just talking about making mistakes." The Director answers, "Both are true! It takes hours of rehearsal for a clown to be ready to make her mistakes golden. A whole lot of hours. My formula is 100 hours of rehearsal for every minute of stage time."

He pauses to let that number sink in. I do the math — even if you were working 40 hours a week it would take three months to make a five-minute clown routine. Ronni gets to the same number at the same moment and we roll our eyes.

"I know my formula sounds crazy to you now. It is crazy. Clowns are a little crazy, but not for the reasons most people think. We're crazy to work so hard to make such short acts." The Director smiles and continues, "We rehearse and rehearse and try to be perfect so that we can be fully aware on stage, moment to moment. A professional clown should go into every show well rehearsed and prepared for golden mistakes. You need to say to yourself, 'When something goes wrong, I have the chance to make my show even get better than what I rehearsed. I have a chance to make a unique and beautiful connection with these people, right now, right here.' A clown is both a workhorse and a hummingbird."

Jake's Journal #4, October 30

The Big Idea:

- For a clown, mistakes should make the act better.

Why does it matter to me?

- I'll never be the best juggler in the world but I might become a great clown if I make GOLDEN mistakes and not stupid mistakes. Connection, not perfection.
- My street patter is messing up my act.

Exercises:

- Rehearse a lot (but not 100 hours/minute, that's just nuts).
- Get more free food by juggling in corner stores.
- Held a handstand, away from the wall, for 7 seconds! Now I'm going for 1 minute.
- Keep working with the strap-on stilt walking (circus skills). With a good costume, I could make money at parties, festivals, maybe even concerts.
- Learned some ballroom dancing – don't know how that fits with clowning but I loved it when our dance teacher showed me how to do a dip. She's stronger than she looks.

My Ah-ha moment:

- Maybe I've been working too hard, or too hard on the wrong things.

CHAPTER SEVEN

PREMIERE
ATLANTA, GEORGIA
Cirque du Soleil

I'M ON AN AIRPORT SHUTTLE heading out of Hartsfield-Jackson Atlanta International Airport. The technicians have been setting up *Corteo's* Grand Chapiteau for a week and now it's time for the cast to arrive. Atlanta is one of the best circus towns in America. Besides being home to the only African-American owned and operated circus in the world, UniverSoul, it hosts long runs of the Ringling shows and New York's Big Apple Circus, not to mention small regional shows, and everyone does good business every year.

We are staying in a hotel that is across the highway from our site. The big blue-and-yellow striped tents loom in the twilight as I walk across a bridge over a couple dozen lanes of traffic. My path takes me through Atlantic Station, an "integrated urban environment" with apartment buildings, grocery stores, banks, restaurants, shops, a movie theater and a central square. The California Pizza Kitchen is draped in orange with life-sized witches guarding the door. I pass a Dillard's, a Pier 1 Imports and a Victoria's Secret, all decked out for Halloween.

I go through security and into the Artistic Tent to sign the call sheet. I'll get one dress rehearsal, tonight, and tomorrow I'll start my first run of shows as the main character in this multimillion-dollar show. My flying acts are under control but I've never rehearsed some of my shorter scenes on stage with lights and sound.

I stretch out, apply my makeup and put on my Act One costume, a shapeless gray 19th-century suit. I tell myself what I tell my students, "Follow in the footsteps of clowns who have gone before." In my case, this means following Antonio, the man who created the role of The

Dead Clown. I will try to do what he did for the last year and a half, the first 450 shows of *Corteo's* long touring schedule.

> Can I make all the cues, even the ones I've never rehearsed? Can I do what I teach when I'm in the spotlight? Can a crumpled old clown hold his own with a bunch of sleek young acrobats?

Before the dress rehearsal audience arrives, I walk around the bleachers, sitting in different seats. I want to get a feel for the audience's point of view. The *Corteo* stage runs right down the middle of the tent with the audience equally divided on either side. People in different seats see a very different show — the center sections see what the director designed while the far side sections get a lot of profiles and peeks into the wings.

After a few minutes, I climb out of the seats to walk the full-sized painted Labyrinth that is the centerpiece of our stage. I carefully avoid acrobats warming up and riggers setting aerial equipment. After the first few turns, I imagine that I'm on the path of a creative life, now heading straight for the center, now veering off and around, getting tantalizingly close and then finding myself quickly on the outer rim in creative exile. From the top of the tent, the labyrinth looks orderly and elegant; walking it is confusing, frustrating and sometimes boring. From afar, my students think I have made it as a professional clown; my life feels very different close up.

The stage manager calls "House is open!" I slip into one of the walkways that tunnel under the audience bleachers, our way of getting from one side of the tent to the other. The tunnels are dark and all of them look alike so it is easy to get lost. I use the tunnels a lot during the show.

I find my way to the Artistic Tent, which is smaller than the Grand Chapiteau. It is mostly open space with blue tumbling mats covering the floor, a large collection of free weights and two exercise bikes in one corner, a trampoline in another and a myriad of pulleys dangling from the ceiling truss for the aerialists to hang their equipment. The men's and women's dressing tables are curtained off with the wardrobe and physical therapy stalls between them.

In one corner of the artistic tent is an incongruously domestic scene, the Tapis Rouge. As the name implies, there is a round red rug, about 15 feet in diameter, with three couches facing a large TV. This is where performers can watch a live feed of the show or pop in a DVD of past performances (every show is videotaped.) Most of the life of the show happens here and in the dining hall, a huge trailer with table seating for 60 and a kitchen big enough for our five cooks to make three meals a day without bumping into each other.

When the stage manager calls "Tapis Rouge!" all 63 of us, including our six-piece band, gather near the red rug, facing a large whiteboard hung just inside the passageway to the Grand Chapiteau. Pointing to a grid of names on the board, the stage manager explains who is doing which track in tonight's performance. A track is what would be called a role if this were a play. In *Corteo* a track includes artistic entrances (scenes where the performer is playing a character) and circus entrances (scenes where the performer is a character in a circus act — acrobatics, juggling, aerial, etc.).

Almost everyone except me has two or more tracks that they do on a regular basis. I am always The Dead Clown. The stage manager has created a complex rotation system that she is constantly updating as the physical therapy department tells her about new injuries.

Once we know who is doing what in the dress rehearsal, the assistant stage manager hands around sheets of paper with the lyrics to "Hey, Jude." The bandleader fires up an electric keyboard and we all sing together. It makes me happy to sing with the cast, even if we have a diversity of pronunciation and pitch.

Before splitting up so each of us can do our final prep for the show, we get in a circle to play a game that involves throwing four-foot pieces of doweling at each other. Years of juggling have given me the right set of skills for "Sticks" and I love the game immediately.

"15 minutes, ladies and gentlemen. 15 minutes."

I quickly write out a cheat sheet for myself. During the show, when I exit all amped up from a scene, I can peek at the sheet to know which way to walk, what costume to put on and where to go for my next entrance. My sheet will get limp with sweat before the first act is over but just knowing it's tucked in the waistband of my underwear helps.

"Places please. Places for dress rehearsal."

Lying on the bed center stage in the dark, I can peek out through the scrims that hide me from both sides of the audience. The rest of the cast is doing pre-show animation, walking through the audience doing tricks and pretending to look for me. They have to hunt for people to play with since there are only a hundred or so folks scattered around the 2,800-seat tent. My heart sinks until I remember that the dress rehearsals are for an invited audience from a few local nonprofits. It really is a rehearsal, not a preview. They even play a CD telling the audience that we may stop the show if there are technical difficulties.

The dress rehearsal is going smoothly, even as the bed tilts forward and back and then flat again. I float up a few yards on my angel-winged wire and then drop down fast. The harness tightens, I pause and then breaststroke as the riggers pull me up in rhythm, as if I were in water. I reach for an angel floating above me and fall again. This time I fly all the way to the top of the tent, to heaven, where Freddo drags me to safety on the catwalk. He unclips my harness, taps me on the shoulder and everything goes black.

Freddo whispers, "Just hold the scaffolding and wait."

I hear his voice; it sounds real. Maybe I'm still alive.

I hold tight to the metal crossbar listening to the buzz of the crowd 50 feet below. Finally, Freddo whispers, "You better climb down — you don't want to be up here if the tent's about to collapse."

In the dark I crawl to the ladder and then down, taking deliberate breaths. I manage to find a tunnel and feel my way to the well-lit Artistic Tent. Someone must have thought to get an emergency generator, for us if not for the audience. The rest of the cast is standing around looking bored. I want to scream, "I'm alive!!" and hug every one of them. I don't.

The stage manager gets our attention. "Here's what I know — the computers that control the flying rig malfunctioned, which blew the lights." I try not to imagine what would have happened if the malfunctioning computers had dropped the flying bed 30 feet to the stage. A Dead Clown.

"The tech crew is trying to reboot the computer. Don't leave the Artistic Tent. I'll keep you posted." We hang around, stretching to stay warm. The audience seems to be happy chatting in the dark. My panic slowly melts into relief; I've made it through the flying act, the audience laughed a little, and the rest of the show is easier for me.

After about 45 minutes, we hear a burst of applause from the house and the stage manager calls us together. "Lights are on, all fixed. We'll do the Dead Clown's flying number again and then continue through to the end of Act One."

I have to fly again?

The stage manager goes on, "We would go home after Act One except that our new Dead Clown is here." He points to me with a flourish; a couple of acrobats clap limply. "It's only fair to give him a chance to do at least a part of Act Two before we throw him in front of 2,800 paying customers tomorrow night." I smile tightly and he continues, "So, after Act One, we'll take a short intermission and pick it up in the middle of Act Two." A couple of huge acrobats wearing only their costume pants glare at me and say something in Russian.

The second time through the flying scene is less scary, but I get shaky climbing down the ladder. After intermission, we start in middle of Act Two and I have to use my cheat sheet after every exit. By the time the night is over, I've performed 11 of my 14 scenes and my big flying number twice. Now my job is to get ready for the premiere tomorrow night. I have to make my cues, stay tuned in to everything and connect with my partners. Just that. Simple.

The next night our premiere goes smoothly, with a full house and no computer glitches. My family is in town for my first show, sitting right up front in the seats normally reserved for friends of Guy Laliberté, the owner of Cirque du Soleil. When I do a short scene in the audience near the Guy seats, my 4-year-old son jumps up and says, "Hi, Dad!" He keeps saying, "Hi, Dad!" and I keep doing my scene. My wife tells me later that when the house lights came up at the end of the show, a woman sitting next to them said "Isn't it cute that your boy thinks the clown is his father." My 9-year-old son apparently explained the whole thing to the woman, who was duly impressed. He then explained to his younger brother that, "You can't talk to Dad when he's working." In the next show, sitting in the same seat but a little more savvy, my younger son jumps up and down staring at me with huge eyes, not saying a word.

Opening a show is always a relief. Somehow my body memorizes every move in a performance much better than in a rehearsal or even a dress rehearsal. But after the second show I feel like something is missing, like I haven't done my job yet. In *Corteo*, I don't do the circus acts I did a decade ago — riding a bike with 10 people on me, juggling clubs while drumming out a rhythm on suitcases, throwing my acrobatic partner around in a dozen odd ways. Performing in this role doesn't make my body feel like it used to after a show. I'll have to get accustomed to not being bruised and exhausted, just scared.

Soon I will have the show deeply in my bones, which is good since I'm going to be alternating performance weeks with Antonio in a complex schedule that will give us both time to be with our families and for me to keep running my school.

Antonio is the reason I'm here. A year ago, when *Corteo* visited San Francisco, I was hired to do some training with the cast and to coach the clown acts. When I was saying good-bye after the last session, Antonio said, "We look a lot alike. You could do this job." I agreed but I also knew that was out of the question. I couldn't leave my family and my school.

A few months later my wife mentioned, as she did periodically, that running a clown school took a whole lot of time but did not pay a whole lot of money. I had to agree and promised to see what I could do about adding some more lucrative work. Remembering my chat with Antonio, I sent a quick email to the Artistic Director offering to substitute for a few weeks now and then if Antonio needed a break. A few hours later, I got a note back offering me the role full-time. Antonio had given notice that he wanted to spend more time with his family.

I waited until my wife and I were away for the weekend, just us, before I brought up the subject of going back on tour. She shocked me by saying, "We'll make this work. Having Cirque du Soleil on your résumé will do things for our family that we can't even imagine. It will be hard but we'll do it." Negotiating the contract, making arrangements for my school and working out childcare took months. Antonio agreed to doing a job-share, I hired teachers and administrators to hold down the fort while I was on the road, and my wife constructed a schedule for her weeks as a single mom. Now we'll see if it all will work.

This first visit is going well, especially for the boys. They love having a bunch of young, well-tattooed acrobats to play with backstage. The trampoline is their favorite spot, bouncing themselves or watching the performers show off for them. Their worlds are expanding with all the languages flying around, the costumes, the rigging, the excitement of the shows and playing with the other kids in the pool at our hotel. My wife was right — this tour is already doing good things for our family.

On Sunday morning, before the matinee, the boys cling to me when I try to load them into the airport shuttle. I tell them, "You have to get back home for school and mom has to work. I'll see you next week." They finally get in the van, stuffed animals and iPods in hand, and I wave as they drive away. Before I even get to the dressing room, my wife calls to tell me that, as the van rode away from the tent, my older son said, "Mommy, open the windows so we can let the pain out."

SPOTLIGHT:
Joel Baker

Joel Baker, a young apprentice barber living in Florida, quit his job, bought a motorcycle and rode west with a friend. After an accident near San Francisco destroyed Joel's bike and gave him a metal clavicle, he started going to acrobatics classes at Circus Center. When we were putting together the second class of The Clown Conservatory, my colleague Peggy Ford told me about this wiry guy who was learning Chinese chair-balancing from the master trainer Lu Yi. "We want Joel." She was right.

A few weeks into the school year, we noticed that Joel brought a small tape recorder to class every day. He explained that he had ADHD — "I'm the kid in kindergarten who thought his name was Dammit Joel." He needed to listen to the tapes every night to make sure he didn't miss anything.

Joel looked funny, walked funny and was a good student. Pretty soon, his classmates were laughing before he started an exercise. About a month into the school year, we asked him to stop being funny so he could focus on learning the techniques of clowning. He was taken aback but, after we assured him he could bring back his funny for the final tour, he agreed. He stuck to his "no funny" vow for months, much to his classmates' disappointment.

About halfway through the school year, Joel asked if he could create a solo piece for his final project rather than a duet or trio as the syllabus stated. We explained to him that on the final tour we wanted to give students a chance to work with other clowns. We consider partnerships the natural environment for clowns even though economic and social factors have led to the majority of American clowns working solo. When Joel pushed, I said that, as the director of the final show, I would be crazy not to take a great solo act if there happened to be one available. He got the point.

Joel worked on his act outside of class and only occasionally checked in with us about a prop or a comic moment he was struggling with. When the time came to choose acts for our final tour, Joel's solo routine was a must-have — a wonderful number with a streetlight that kept turning on and off as he tried to read a book. His funny was back in full force but now with the structures, skills and rhythms of a professional clown. A decade and a half later, he is doing the streetlight act again — incorporating new ideas with a hand-balancing lamp — in Germany, after performing with some of the best circuses in the world, including the Pickle Circus, Les 7 doigts de la main and a couple of thousand shows as a Nowhere Man in Cirque du Soleil's *LOVE*.

CHAPTER EIGHT

GRAPEFRUIT
The Clown Conservatory

9:05 MONDAY MORNING. It's freezing. Anita looks like she's ready to run the Iditarod — down jacket, mittens, hand-knit cap, ski pants and giant fuzzy 49ers slippers. I leave my sweatshirt on to straddle-stretch on the mats. Groin muscles scream. Ease off a little. "Jake, be strong!" Sneak a sip of tea. "Handstand, Jake. Too lazy today." Blood rushes to my head. Ten seconds is all I can do, even up against the wall. I'm a mess.

Last night a bunch of us went to the Mission District for burritos and dancing. Ronni and I tried to dance the samba but ended up doing ballroom moves we learned in class with some added hip action. It got sexy. Our thighs were touching. I went to get a couple of beers and when I came back, Ronni was dancing with Virginie. Their thighs were touching. I drank both beers. They were touching more than thighs. I left. Dan followed after me and we went to a bar to commiserate.

This morning I walked all the way to Noriega Street to catch the 7 Haight bus so I didn't have to see Ronni before class. Then she was a couple of minutes late for acrobatics so I was already stretching when she walked in. We haven't looked at each other all morning. Virginie, who's wearing lots of leather with some big holes to show off her tattoos, doesn't seem to be paying Ronni any extra attention. Maybe I'm overreacting. Maybe I'm hung over.

By dance class, my head is feeling better and I'm thankful that I had to come to school today. If I'd had a choice, I'd be home right now wallowing in pain. The "discipline of acrobatics" may be good for performers; it is also good for hangovers and broken hearts.

Now we're done with our barre work — plie, tendu, grand battement — and we're ready to review our ballroom moves. Virginie is my first partner. As we jitterbug, she whispers, "We missed you last night." I pretend I don't hear her. I avoid Ronni right up until our last dance, when the teacher chooses the two of us to demonstrate a waltz chassé across the floor. I'm stiff and awkward.

The class ends. I put on my coat, grab my backpack and almost make it out. "Jake, want to eat lunch at Kezar?" I don't answer and walk out the back door of the studio that leads right onto Frederick Street. The wet wind hits my sweaty face. Ronni walks beside me. Without saying anything, we go to Kezar, a high school football stadium across the street. The class uses the field to train for arena shows like Ringling Bros. & Barnum and Bailey. On warmer days, students eat lunch in the bleachers.

Ronni and I sit on the metal bench and stare at the football field. "Jake, you don't have to pretend I don't exist. It was fun dancing with you last night and it was fun dancing with other people." I just sit and stare. "Why did you and Dan go off in a huff?"

"We didn't go off in a huff, we just wanted to get away from that music. Too loud to think." This sounds like bullshit even to me.

"Come on, don't be such a jerk. We're friends. We need each other. We don't need romantic bullshit."

"Maybe you don't need romantic bullshit but maybe I do."

"You don't want romance with me. Really. I'm bad at romance."

"Could have fooled me last night."

"That's just goofing around. Once it gets serious, I always mess it up." Ronni turns to look at me. "Jake, we're friends and we're clown partners. We could last a lifetime if we don't fuck it up."

I want to kiss her but I just sit there staring at the goalposts.

"Jake, look at me. This is serious shit."

She's right. A clown partner is special. No place for romance. Maybe I can ask one of the aerialists out. They're cuter than Ronni. Or Virginie. It's freezing out here. I turn and give Ronni a hug. We cry and shake hands and then go back inside to eat lunch. We're partners.

When the Director comes in to start class, we are all huddled under the large wall-mounted heater. He says, "Since our last show, your other classes have been focused on improvisation — theatrical improvisation, dance improvisation and improvisation with music. But you've got another show in three weeks so we'd better get to work on some routines. We wouldn't want to have nothing to offer the audience, like last time."

No one laughs.

"I need help from one of you." Virginie kicks up to a handstand and walks, upside-down, to center stage. The Director says, "Beautiful! Now hold that handstand for a moment while I explain to the class." Virginie is taking quick steps with her hands, trying to find the balance, but her feet don't come down. "Virginie and I will do the routine called Grapefruit."

Roger says, "Grapefruit? Where did that name come from?"

"Don't ask, I don't remember. It was the '70s, it was Berkeley…" I try to imagine our burly, greying director as a teenage hippie. Upstage, Virginie slides out of her handstand into a split; the Director helps her up and whispers something to her as they walk to the far right side of the stage. They stop, she nods and he says, "We are now ready for Grapefruit."

The Director walks to center stage with Virginie right behind him. He starts to give an energetic lecture on comedy. She imitates him. A couple of sentences into his spiel, he notices her and stops talking. He then picks her up by her leather shirt collar and walks her offstage to where they started. He puts her down and says, "Stay!"

The Director walks back on stage, Virginie follows and they do exactly the same thing, with Virginie's gestures getting larger and more mocking before the Director takes her offstage and tells her to "Stay!" again.

The third time, the Director comes center and sees Virginie just before he starts talking. He freezes and stares at her. Virginie looks puzzled for a moment and then continues to imitate him but now in French. She gestures wildly and I can make out a few words — "merde," "Jacques Tati," "Jerry Lewis." She takes a breath and peeks at the Director, who is still just staring at her. Virginie turns around, pulls down her torn jeans and moons us. A full moon.

We laugh but the Director doesn't move.

Virginie pulls up her pants, buckles her studded belt and looks at the Director. They stare at each other for a moment and the thought crosses my mind, "She's going to get kicked out of class." But the Director doesn't move and, after what seems like a full minute, Virginie sighs, picks herself up by the collar, walks herself off stage and tells herself, "Stay!" The Director holds still for one more moment, looking at her, and then quickly finishes his lecture.

We have never seen Virginie so funny and we let her know it. With the Director as her partner, forced into the simple structure of Grapefruit, all her craziness is really funny. The Director says, "Working with a partner is the natural state for most clowns. Virginie is a good partner, even if she is a pain in the ass." Virginie curtsies.

"This is the simplest two-person routine I know, a basic three beat with a No. 1 clown, me, and a No. 2 clown, Virginie. The No. 1 is coming out to do something with the audience, in this case a lecture but it could be anything. The No. 2 wants to join in. Simple. The essence of Grapefruit is the interruption, the time between starting an action and finishing it — I started a lecture but Virginie interrupted me and that interruption was the whole routine. The moment before No. 2 takes herself offstage is usually the most fun, and, as you could see, Virginie took full advantage." Virginie curtsies again.

"In some traditions, these clown roles are called the White Clown," he points to himself, "and the Auguste" he points to Virginie, "or the White and the Red. In any case, the No. 1 thinks he knows what is going on, he is sure he's the leader. The No. 2 can't or won't follow the rules. Virginie is a natural No. 2 because she doesn't like to follow rules in real life." Virginie jumps up and would have mooned us again if the Director hadn't put his hand on her shoulder and said, "Virginie, let's switch roles. Do you remember the routine?"

"Oui, mon deuxième," and Virginie throws a cartwheel, landing where the Director had started the routine the first time. The Director stands behind her and what happens next is completely different from the first time, even though they do the same Grapefruit routine. Virginie comes onstage singing some French techno-punk anthem and the Director, playing the No.2, tries to imitate her. The third time, Virginie just stares as the Director mangles the French song, head jerking and body flailing. He finally takes himself offstage and says, "Stay!" Virginie sings the final note and we applaud.

Amazing. This simple routine has some kind of clown magic — it was funny both times and they didn't have to rehearse for 100 hours. Take a Grapefruit, add clowns and, voilà, laughter.

"Time to get to work, everyone! Pair up, take off your coats and try some Grapefruit."

Ronni grabs my arm. "Let me be the No. 1. I'll juggle and you can steal my balls." We both take off one layer of clothing and practice the routine a few times. I keep finding more ways to steal the balls until the Director says, "Now switch roles. Remember, do the structure, the scheme of the gag, exactly the same each time."

I become a strict old No. 1 while Ronni's No. 2 darts around like a malicious mosquito. It's pretty funny so we add a bit where Ronni takes me offstage instead of the other way around, and then we do a big juggling finale instead of Ronni saying, "Stay!"

In front of the class, our Grapefruit routine starts strong, but by the time we get to our big juggling finale, the applause is polite at best.

Clown magic my ass.

As we sit down, the Director says, "Ronni and Jake, your partnership is strong and your juggling is good. Now you need to stick with the simple logic. Don't try to outsmart the routine. The scheme of the gag is a limitation, and limitations are great for artists."

Dan and Anita are up next, with Dan as a unicycle riding No. 1 and Anita as his overdressed dancing sidekick. They do the routine flawlessly, neatly choreographed and graceful, even with all the extra clothes. I'm impressed.

They give each other a hug and start to sit down but the Director stops them, "You did the scheme of the gag exactly — thank you. Now try it again without changing anything, except this time focus on each other. Anita, you want desperately to be a unicycle star like Dan; Dan, you want desperately to entertain us and you need Anita to stay out of your way. Add this internal life to the wonderful structure you already have."

Dan pulls his Atlanta Hawks sweatshirt over his head, revealing a well-worn tee from his youth circus days; Anita adjusts her mittens. The routine is still as neat and graceful but now there are glimpses of real people on stage — Dan is alternately angry and charming while Anita adds some raw ambition to her habitual poise. The Director gives them each a high five on the way offstage.

Roger and Starlight get up and immediately Roger becomes a snarling, villainous No. 1, yelling at us like a drill sergeant. Starlight wins our sympathy by imitating him and then taking the full blast of his anger without flinching. She reminds me of Alice in "The Honeymooners" when Jackie Gleason threatens to hit her. Starlight finishes the routine with a sly bow and we cheer.

"Nice. A hard-ass No. 1 with a completely sympathetic No. 2. That works. Now try switching roles."

Dan, who is a circus history geek, interrupts, "Don't clowns find one character and then play it for life? Shouldn't we be finding our character instead of switching roles?"

"Yes, you are right, Dan. They taught you well at Circus Smirkus." Dan smiles and points to his tee shirt. "Many clowns find a character that works and make a career of that. At this stage in your growth, though, you need to explore the possibilities. Anita, you are a natural acrobatic flyer." Anita, who is barely five feet and 100 pounds after a big lunch, says, "Yes, of course."

"But in acrobatics class, you are learning all three roles — porter, flyer and spotter."

True. In class this week, we learned a trick where the porter lies on her back and the flyer sits on her feet. Anita could hold Virginie, Ronni and even Roger. She's been bragging about it all week.

"Anita becomes a better flyer by knowing the porter position. You will all be a better clown by learning both clown roles."

Starlight and Roger start again. No matter how tough Starlight tries to be as No. 1, she still gets our sympathy and Roger is surprisingly sweet as a No. 2.

"Nicely done. We were rooting for both of you. You both treated us, the audience, like we are your best friends. Even though you were completely at odds with each other, we could still love you both. Laurel and Hardy were great at this, and so are you."

The Director gives us 30 minutes to rework our routines. Ronni and I are determined to keep the scheme of the gag, focus on each other and treat the audience as our best friends. And juggle.

When we show our routine again, the class laughs a lot and the Director congratulates us. "Now you're getting it. Respect the gag and good things happen."

Ronni and I smile. This simple, simple gag — so damn simple — seems to have infinite variations. Even though we only rehearsed for an hour, we got real laughs and the Director liked it. We improved a lot from the first try by doing less and following the rules. With a few hundred hours of rehearsal, maybe we could get a circus contract.

Jake's Journal #5, November 10

Big Idea:
- *Classic clown routines are corny but they really work.*

Why does it matter to me?
- *Clown routines are easy to learn and open source.*
- *These routines might be my ticket to a circus contract.*

Other Routines:
- *Close walks = walking right behind someone. Advanced level = have your chest touching their back. Super Advanced = throw in a hitch kick. Good for shows; also to practice putting your full attention on another performer, getting exactly in sync with their body's rhythm.*
- *Slaps = the basics of clowning. One person slaps (stop hand before you hit their nose); other person claps their hands a millisecond before moving their head like they've been hit (called "taking the nap"). Do it right, it looks great; otherwise, it's totally fake-o. Lots of variations — side slap, front slap, slaps and falls, three beat slap routine, etc.*

What I need to rehearse:
- *Keep working on the 'Grapefruit' routine with Ronni for the show at the end of the month.*
- *Practice the other routines with anyone who will stay after class.*
- *Practice doing two highs and dive rolls for the acrobatics act.*
- *Run through the dance routine with the music EVERY time (need to rehearse at school, my room's too small).*

Ah-ha Moment:
- *Clowns follow rules sometimes and that's funny sometimes — "Don't mess with the scheme of the gag."*
- *Don't date your clown partner!*

CHAPTER NINE

THE MARIONETTE
HOUSTON, TEXAS

Cirque du Soleil

I'M SITTING IN A STRADDLE-STRETCH in the middle of the Artistic Tent, getting ready for the first show of the week here in Houston. Settling back into the touring life is hard. When I shadowed Antonio, my predecessor, in D.C. I saw that he had little moments with everyone backstage — handshakes with acrobats, jokes with the riggers in French, kisses for the aerialists, teaching the jugglers to curse in Italian. This routine of tiny rituals kept him connected to the rest of the cast and crew every show. Antonio was the Papa of the company.

Then I took over, completely consumed with trying to enter at the right time, in the right costume, without having any rituals backstage, and speaking only English. Everyone missed Antonio. Having someone new join a cast is always jarring; when the new Papa is too busy to connect, things fall apart. I was saved by folks who took the time to connect with me in those first few weeks — the band leader who helped me tune the glass harmonica every show, the rigger who always waved at me from the wings as I flew the bike across the stage, the acrobat who shook my hand through the curtain right before she went on. By now I have my own rituals and I'm trying to do my part connecting with the new folks.

I'm amazed at how important the offstage routines are. We have rituals to stay safe like double-checking the harnesses and standing clear of the rigging lines, and we have rituals that keep our hearts connected. Some of mine have a whiff of superstition, like getting onto the giant trampoline after Fred but before Jamar, and some feel illicit, like blowing kisses from high in the air with a Russian flyer, the wife of an acrobatic trainer, who has never said more than a two words to me offstage. This touring life is lonely, boring and scary; these moments of ritual and human connection are my lifeline.

The Artistic Director, who is wearing his usual chic workout ensemble with the addition of a Santa hat and red cowboy boots, walks behind me. He gently pushes on my back to increase the stretch and the Santa hat falls in my lap. I hand it back.

"Thanks. I forgot to wear it at Christmas and it goes perfectly with my new boots, don't you think?"

He puts the hat back on and pushes me a little harder into my stretch. I make "that's enough" kind of noises, which he ignores. He finally lets me up and says, "In the Marionette act, think like a dancer." I'm not sure what he means but before I can ask, he's off to work with the acrobatic dance duet.

The Artistic Director is a retired dancer and, except for a few white hairs, he looks like he could still dance a full-length ballet. Although our backgrounds are very different, we get along well and have developed an unwritten arrangement — I try every performance note he gives me and, if it doesn't work, we talk about it after the show. Half the time his notes work really well and the other half he is willing to adjust or let go of his idea, which gives me the room I need as a performer.

But I hate the Marionette act. It starts beautifully when an acrobat dressed in a Harlequin costume floats down from the top of the tent. She is suspended on cords from a contraption that looks like a giant metal spider. The human Marionette lands on the stage and does some loose-limbed flips, giving the audience the idea that they are in for a magical circus act performed by a living puppet.

Then I enter. I'm dressed in a particularly unflattering 19th-century wool bathing suit and I'm kicking a beach ball. I pretend to play soccer with the Marionette until she steals my beach ball and flies back up to the top of the tent. That's it; that's the routine. It is never magical and sometimes it is a total flop.

> "Think like a dancer." If I were a dancer, not a clown or actor, what would I do with the Marionette? How would I dance with her? How would I dance with the ball? How would I move in my ugly bathing suit?

In the show, I enter with my beach ball and focus on dancing — smooth movement then sharp, coming close to the Marionette and farther way. I think about high and low, fast and slow. I think in the language of dance and the routine goes much better. Not yet magic, but better.

It's now Friday, late, and I'm back in my room having a snack of chips and anchovy dip, my favorite road indulgence. I take a rich, salty bite, grateful to be a large clown and not a tiny dancer. The Marionette routine was good today, both shows. I was dancing with a human puppet and a beach ball, really dancing. Francine, a gorgeous French gymnast who has a tattoo of the Olympic logo on her shoulder, played the Marionette today. As we were leaving the tent, she gave me a double cheek kiss, adding a whispered, 'Merci bien, mon Clown de Morts." Dancing does have some advantages over clowning.

We've got two shows tomorrow and it is late but I still have a couple of hours of work at my day job, running The Clown Conservatory. I start with the fun part — sending emails to my students:

> "Clowning is an omnivorous and demanding art form. We clowns need a lot of different skills and we can use almost any other discipline in our clowning. If we are lucky, we work in many different situations, not all of which will be pure clowning. Being able to speak circus in all its forms, as well music and theater and especially dance, is important for us. This is one of the reasons you are learning so many different skills at The Clown Conservatory."

I decide they don't need to know about the French cheek kisses so I hit "send." Next, I spend an hour or so on the daily work of a school director: putting some preliminary numbers into the budget for next year, reviewing the minutes from the last faculty meeting and the never-ending job of recruiting new students, which tonight means sending emails to theater professors who have recommended students in the past.

I'm about to close my laptop when my in-box pings and I can't resist reading an email from Guillaume, our wonderfully witty French clown teacher. It's a scalding critique of one of our students. Guillaume is never politic and this email to the faculty holds nothing back. I read it with the guilty thrill one gets from a well-written, vicious review of someone else's show. Then I notice that he has sent it to the student listserv, not to the faculty.

The anchovies churn in my stomach. We will lose students — certainly Virginie, the target of the screed, and possibly others who have already complained about my extended absences. We are at the minimum enrollment needed to cover our budget, even with me virtually volunteering. This could close my school.

Hours later I hit "send" on an email to the faculty, staff and students:

> "Guillaume's email mistake gives me an opportunity to talk about how we approach teaching at The Clown Conservatory. First off, we staff members always discuss individual students and your work in detail and critically. This is how a professional school should work. I often find myself defending student clown pieces, explaining what each student is working on at the moment and why I think their work is going in the right direction. Had we talked in person, my reaction to Guillaume would have been to say that Virginie was responding to a challenge I gave her, even though it was very uncomfortable for her. I would have said that he was critiquing an act as if it were a product and not part of a process.
>
> "Challenges from other staff members keep me honest, too, and all of us regularly change our approach to a student's work in response to these often contentious sessions. Usually, this all stays in the staff meeting and in our conversations with each other. Sometimes we make mistakes and hit the wrong send button."

I will fly home after the second show on Sunday and face the music from my students on Monday morning. Maybe I can distract them, dazzle them so they forget the nasty email. I say a little prayer to the god of clown schools, brush the anchovies out of my teeth and head to bed.

SPOTLIGHT:
Carlo and Orlene Gentile

Orlene Gentile was in the first class of The Clown Conservatory; her husband Carlo came the next year. After graduating, they went to Hebei, China, to study foot-juggling and then started performing professionally.

A few years later I visited them on Circus Monti, where Orlene was doing her solo foot-juggling act, lying on a specially made stand while spinning a table, among other things, on her feet. Carlo was taking care of their new baby and managing their wheeled home, a classic Swiss caravan that was a quite a few cuts above an Airstream.

Circus Monti is a small family circus that tours German-speaking Switzerland. The show was full of young performers who had recently graduated from circus schools around the world — Montreal, Paris, San Francisco. Backstage at intermission, Orlene unsnapped a specially made flap on her costume so she could nurse. The baby was still happily sucking away when the stage manager called 'Fünf Minuten!' The baby sucked on until, with only moments to spare, Carlo and Orlene executed a well-rehearsed routine that ended with Carlo, a happy baby and me back in our seats with Orlene back on stage, fully clothed.

The growing Gentile family continues to live on the road, now traveling in a large American RV and spending most of their time stateside. The children are in the act, getting thrown around on their parents' feet.

Carlo, Orlene and their children are living a life that was typical a few decades ago, when most artists came from families that traveled and performed together for generations. Although there have always been outsiders in American circus, it is only in the last 30 years that the majority of performers are, like me, first-generation. The Gentiles are going back to an earlier time in circus history.

CHAPTER TEN

COMEDY OF ERRORS
The Clown Conservatory

THE STREETCAR CRAWLS INTO the Sunset District, packed with the Friday night getaway crowd. This first week back at school, after a short 10-day vacation home in New Jersey, has kicked my ass. I should have worked out at my parents' house a couple of times over the holidays, even gone to their gym. Oh, well. I get off a stop early to escape the Suits and walk the three blocks home. With the wet wind coming in off the ocean, I'm colder here than in the snow back East.

I unlock my apartment door, climb the stairs and go to my room to dump my backpack on the bed. Thankfully my roommates are out of town for the weekend so I blast the heat and head for the kitchen to raid the fridge. Halfway through a container of week-old take-out pad Thai, I wander back to my room and boot up my laptop.

Nestled among the spam and e-newsletters is an email from the French Master. I open it up, read the first line and drop my fork on the floor.

"Virginie is, of course, completely self-absorbed and useless as a clown."

He goes on, ripping my classmate to shreds. About halfway through the second paragraph, he refers to "yesterday's faculty meeting" and I realize this is meant for the teachers, not for us. A huge email mistake. I re-read it a few times.

Finally, I pick up my fork, finish the pad Thai and start calling my classmates. We talk about demanding a public apology or making the Director write a letter to the whole school explaining why the faculty is so abusive or going on strike or... I am pissed and scared when I think about what the teachers must be saying about me. Ronni calls and says that the Director just sent an email, which she reads to me over the phone. "We always discuss your work in detail and critically." I blurt out, "Shit, the teachers are talking about me and it isn't good." Ronni tells me to stop being such a narcissist, that the Director is framing the French Master's email in the context of the school's approach to faculty feedback. We hang up on a sour note.

All weekend, the two emails and the call with Ronni keep eating at me. My father used to come home with stories about the intrigues and backbiting in his physics department; maybe clowning isn't so different. I think about how Virginie must be feeling but I don't give her a call.

Before I open the door to the classroom this Monday morning, holding a cup of hot Lipton's in one hand and my pack full of juggling equipment in the other, I hear Virginie's high-pitched laugh. I walk in and am shocked to see her standing in the middle of the room hugging the French Master. As they jabber away in French, I walk over to Ronni and give her a "what gives?" kind of look. She shrugs. Starlight comes over and tells us that she had gone right to Virginie's apartment on Friday when the emails arrived, expecting to find her in tears. Instead, Virginie told Starlight that she was finally getting the tough feedback she had expected when she came to San Francisco. Starlight raises her eyebrows and gives us a nod that could mean either "She's nuts" or "She's so deep."

Roger and Anita come in and go right to the French Master. Snippets of English float my way, "...do you think...," "Tell me...," "Don't sugar coat..." They want to be ripped to shreds too. The Director walks in and, as he approaches the French Master, the students turn and walk away. The two old clowns move to a corner of the room and talk in whispers.

A moment later, the French Master calls us together in the middle of the mat and apologizes for sending the email to all of us instead of to the faculty. He pointedly does not apologize for what he said in the email. Virginie gives him a sly smile, which he returns as the Director steps forward. He looks tired.

"Some schools would regularly share harsh critiques like Guillaume's with their students." He nods to the French Master. "And some of you may want these kind of critiques." He looks at Virginie, who says, "Bien sûr." The Director continues, "While I understand the idea behind this, I don't agree with the philosophy. Finding one's unique voice while learning a myriad of skills is not a pretty process. Unless you all are comfortable making mistakes, you will never find a true voice. It is hard to get comfortable when mistakes get so viciously critiqued."

He gives the French Master a sideways glance, which is met with a hard stare. The Director continues, "I have a deep faith in the power of audiences to teach us, if we can learn to listen to them. This is why our program has so many shows. The audience will tell you when you are heading in the wrong direction more eloquently than your teachers."

Surprisingly, the French Master says, "This is true, of course. Nothing I say will hurt as much as a little 'boo' or hearing the crickets instead of the laughs."

The Director chuckles and I begin to wonder if these two didn't plan this whole email mistake together. The Director turns to Virginie. "When you and I trust each other more, when you know in your bones that I have your best interests in my heart, I will tell you what I think about your work in no uncertain terms." Virginie sneers. "Merci bien."

The Director smiles and adds, "Only if you ask me. And I won't send an email." The French Master feigns offense and storms out of the room, "accidentally" hitting the doorjamb on the way. We all laugh; he re-enters to take a bow, and exits.

We look back and the Director is not smiling. "I want you all to have 50-year careers and I want to be with you all the way." I start to laugh at the thought of a career that lasts a half a century but the Director stops me. "I'm serious. Fifty years. And I want comps for all your shows. Let's get to work."

The Director brushes past me and hops onto the stage. He sweeps a paisley-patterned cloth off of a long folding table, revealing a couple dozen grotesque masks.

Commedia dell'arte! Nasty emails and clown conspiracies are now old news. Commedia dell'arte is where Western clowning began, the root of everything we do! I jump onstage to see the masks. A few names pop into my mind — Harlequin, Isabella, The Captain — but I can't match these names to faces in this jumble of huge painted noses, strange eyeholes and sculpted cheeks. I reach to pick up a mustachioed mask with a long phallic nose but the Director stops me.

"Not yet, Jake." Then, turning to the class, he adds, "You'll all have a chance to try on the masks soon enough. First let me introduce you to the characters of the Italian Comedy." The Director spins around and grabs another mask off the table. It is on his face when he turns back.

"My name is Il Dottore. I am an expert in…everything." The Director is wearing a mask that covers his forehead and nose. His voice is pitched higher, with an Italian accent, and when he makes a grand gesture with his hand it almost knocks him off balance. He recovers and continues, unfazed.

"My colleagues and I were born in 16th-century Italian marketplaces. It was a magical moment when circus, theater, music and the dance intertwined to create that most beloved of forms, Commedia dell'arte!" Another grand gesture, another precarious tilt, and he continues, "Troupes of exquisitely skilled players embodied archetypal characters, such as myself, Il Dottore." A clumsy bow. "We enacted classic scenarios with improvised dialogue and beautifully crafted routines called *lazzi*." He enjoys the word "lazzi" so much he repeats it for 30 seconds, finding new ways to say it each time.

"These *lazzi*…" We all groan, waiting for him to play with the word again. Instead, he goes on, "The word *lazzi*, by the way, is plural for *lazzo*. You see, in *Italiano*, the masculine singular ending of 'o' becomes an 'i,' pronounced '*ee*,' when it is pluralized. Therefore, the singular *lazzo* becomes, in the plural…"

Dan shouts, "Il Dottore, please tell us more about Commedia dell'arte."

Il Dottore freezes and, while holding his body still, snaps his head to look at Dan. The mask seems to bristle in anger. Suddenly, Il Dottore smiles and makes another grand, awkward bow. It is so strange, and happens so quickly, that we laugh. Another spin, the mask is gone and the Director is back.

"Thank you, Dan, for demonstrating a key similarity between Commedia and clowning — playing with the audience. Audiences for the original Commedia troupes paid after the show, if they paid at all. You are very motivated to listen and learn from every audience when your dinner depends on keeping that audience so entertained that they'll put money in your hat at the end of the show."

Bari and I look at each other and nod — we've been there in our street shows.

Another spin and Il Dottore is back. "Clowns, which in *Italiano* is *pa-*

gliacci, created routines, which in *Français* is *entrées*. These *pagliacci entrées* come from 16th-century *lazzi*, which, in *Italiano*, is the plural of…"

I shout, "We know!"

He freezes, tips his head, turns to glare directly at me, and then does a take to Dan, who giggles, and finally Il Dottore does his clumsy bow.

"We, the characters of Commedia dell'arte, are the grandparents of you, modern-day *pagliacci*, my little clowns!" Il Dottore puffs himself up and shouts, "I am your *nonno*! You are my *nipoti*…" He suddenly shifts back to his pedant stance, "…which is the plural of *nipoto*, which means 'grandchild' in *Italiano*. You see, in *Italiano*, which comes from the Latin *ita*, the plural is formed by…"

We all shout, "We know!"

Il Dottore suddenly deflates entirely, looks furtively around the room and starts to turn away from us. In the last moment, he puffs back up, gives his clumsy bow, and turns his back to us. We applaud.

Jake's Journal #6, January 8

Big Idea:

- *Commedia dell'arte is what 16th century street performers did. I am truly their grandchild.*

Why is it important to me?

- *This Commedia stuff might help me figure out how to make a clown character.*

Concepts:

- *Commedia dell'arte rehearsed scenes = lazzi (plural of lazzo)*
- *Improvise between lazzi*
- *There is no "fourth wall" in Commedia or clowning — the audience is part of the scene*

Ah-ha Moment:

- *Some people actually WANT to get their work ripped to shreds by the teachers. Maybe I'm too soft. Maybe they are too hard.*

CHAPTER ELEVEN

AN ITALIAN INTERLUDE
Cirque du Soleil

I HAVE LANDED IN THE BIRTHPLACE of Commedia dell'arte. Before starting our run in Dallas, Cirque du Soleil gave me a plane ticket to Italy, or, to be precise, the Italian part of Switzerland. Tomorrow, I'm scheduled to meet the man who created *Corteo*.

I laugh out loud driving my tiny rent-a-car out of the airport parking lot and onto streets clogged with bike riders and lined with grapevines and grazing donkeys. My route takes me along the shores of Lago Maggiore, whose waters seem to spawn physical theater geniuses: Dimitri's famous school and theater is nearby and the Nobel prize winning clown and playwright Dario Fo was born on the Italian shore of the lake. Dominico, the man I'm here to see, may be a genius too.

The next day, I meet my Artistic Director in the hotel lobby and we drive to a small lakeside town. We park in front of an old stone building, four stories tall, overlooking the water. A tall man in his 50s lets us in and tells us that he is an actor in the company. "Dominico is running late. His wife is back in the hospital. Can I make you a coffee while we wait?" A tiny theater, with only two rows of seats, is on the bottom floor and there is a kitchen next to the theater. We sit in the kitchen drinking thick black coffee. The caffeine amps up the excitement I already feel waiting to meet a man steeped in the traditions of Arlecchino, Colombina and Il Dottore.

After an hour or so, Dominico arrives with black circles under his eyes, boyishly curly hair and an open, warm manner. He pours himself a coffee, joins us at the table and starts to talk about his approach to theater.

The performers in *Corteo* who spent eight months rehearsing with Dominico all speak fondly of him, but they warned me that he can talk for hours about theater and make no sense at all. According to all of them his English is undecipherable and his ideas are incomprehensible.

Now Dominico is speaking beautifully accented English and making perfect sense. But I understand why my cast-mates didn't understand him; Dominico comes from a complex theatrical background, including a big dose of Grotowski, the great Polish director/teacher, as well as film acting concepts and some clowning. In the early rehearsals of *Corteo*, the performers, many of whom have no background in theater, could easily have thought he was speaking gibberish.

I'm happy to understand him but disappointed that he doesn't even mention Commedia dell'arte. I have never been a big Grotowski fan and film acting is not my forte.

After Dominico downs a few cups of coffee he leads us all into the theater. My Artistic Director and the tall actor sit in the audience. Dominico carefully places two chairs center stage, facing each other, asks me to sit in one of them and walks into the wings to fiddle with some switches. Suddenly the theater goes dark and then, a moment later, a single spotlight blinds me. Dominico sits across from me in the dark and starts to talk about the videos he's been watching of my performances in *Corteo*.

"You do not understand The Dead Clown. You are too showy, too American. You need to learn to be perfectly natural on stage."

I am hurt. I had fooled myself into thinking this would be a meeting of two seasoned artists — the creator and me, the man who was bringing his creation to life. Instead, I'm sitting on a dark stage in a spotlight getting lectured to like a first-year student. My face gets wet and clammy under the heat of the light.

When I can listen again, Dominico is saying I need to use my eyes only, like a movie actor. "Feel the scene inside and only let the emotion come out through your eyes. Do less, less, less!"

What does he mean by less? Movie acting in front of a big circus audience doesn't make sense.

He also wants me to be "more Alexei." Alexei is a wild-man Uzbek acrobat, brilliant onstage and a hyperactive shit-disturber backstage. About a week after I took over the Dead Clown role, Alexei pulled me aside and said, "Why do you give 100 percent on stage? You make it bad for the rest of us. They only want 75 percent." I was a bit shocked, especially since Alexei looks like he's giving 100 percent every night. I finally spit out the only answer that came to mind: "I give 75 percent for Cirque du Soleil and the other 25 percent is for me, so I feel like an artist and not a hired hand." Alexei walked away, mumbling in Russian, but he didn't challenge me again and we became good friends. It seems Dominico wants me to be more disruptive, a pain in the ass instead of a leader, a contrarian clown offstage as well as onstage. This is exactly what I try hard to convince my students not to do.

Now Dominico is saying that it isn't important for me to use the same lines or do the exact same actions every night. "You must connect directly with each performer at every moment." This makes more sense.

Before I can agree with him, he is off on a long tangent describing a day on the beach when he was a boy and how he loved to play soccer. I'm confused. Now he's onto the magic of puppets and I realize that he is talking about the Marionette act.

"In that act, you must be natural, just like you are now. You see, we have been talking for an hour onstage, under the lights, with an audience of two, and you have been perfectly natural the whole time. Do the same thing in *Corteo* in front of 3,000 people."

Dominico jumps up, turns on all the lights and grabs a soccer ball. He kicks it to me and I try to dribble it. I didn't play soccer as a kid so I'm embarrassingly clumsy. After 20 minutes of kicking the ball back and forth, he sets up a scene — he is the Marionette and I start running around him, passing and dribbling.

"Say something! Talk to me."

Even as I'm panting, sweating and improvising, I think, "Ah yes, this is an old Grotowski trick of getting an actor physically exhausted to get to a deeper, more natural way of acting."

We go on and on until Dominico suddenly grabs the soccer ball and walks away. My Artistic Director follows him into the dressing room. I stand there, alone onstage, dripping sweat.

He wants me to be a pain in the ass backstage. He wants me to improvise and connect with the other performers onstage. He wants me to do less, to use my eyes like a movie actor.

The idea of doing less, of being more natural, makes me think of my old acrobatic trainer, Lu Yi. Decades ago, after he'd watched me perform with the Pickle Family Circus for a few months, Lu Yi took me aside and said, "You have two clowns — an outside one and an inside one. You need to show more of the inside one." It's embarrassing to realize that I'm still struggling with the same challenge I faced in my 30s. But I agree with Dominico and Lu Yi: I need more inside clown.

The rest of what Dominico wants from me doesn't make sense. Clearly what I'm doing in *Corteo* every night is not what he wants, but I might not be able to do what he wants. I think of my students when they give me that look that says, "You've just asked me to do the impossible."

"My Dead Clown, please come look at this."

I follow Dominico's voice into the costume shop. He is holding up a beautiful, slightly moth-eaten European White Clown costume. It has a bolero-like jacket with bloomer pants covered in thousands of white sequins. Whoever wore this costume would have added a full white face with dainty red and black accents, a conical hat and high heels. This is the look that evolved in the late 19th century for the No. 1, the straight man, in classic European clown routines.

Dominico says, "My mentor gave me this costume. It was my inspiration for the show." My Artistic Director and I make the appropriately appreciative noises. "Now let's eat." The tall actor, who must have gone to the kitchen instead of the costume shop, has made pasta and a salad. We sit down to enjoy the food with, of course, lots of good red wine.

Dominico is distracted as he eats and I wonder if he's trying to figure out how to say, "We have found a replacement for you" in English. Finally he says, "Keep practicing glass harmonica." I start to mutter something about loving the feel of the glasses vibrating under my fingers but Dominico turns to my Artistic Director and says, "You must tell the band to stop playing the same notes on keyboard. Let the audience hear the clown play, even when he plays badly." I am both insulted and thrilled. "Cirque du Soleil thinks that being perfect is interesting — it is not. What is interesting is real people doing real things, making real mistakes." My Artistic Director smiles politely and I think, "Dominico could be teaching my lesson on golden mistakes right now."

Dominico's phone rings, he says a few words in rapid Italian, hangs up and turns to me. "The doctors have finished their work so I will take my wife home now. Thank you for coming all this way to visit with me, my Dead Clown. Since my time still belongs to my wife's doctors, I may not see you again. Play well." The other two men walk Dominico to his car, leaving me to pour myself another glass of wine. Maybe I still have a job.

SPOTLIGHT:
Lu Yi

In March 1990, the deputy Director of Acrobats for all of China came to live in San Francisco. Lu Yi had been a world-class acrobat in his youth and then cemented his fame directing the Nanjing Acrobatic Troupe. He brought his wife and two teenage daughters with him. They were lured to California by Judy Finelli, then artistic director of the Pickle Family Circus and much later, circus skills teacher at The Clown Conservatory. Lu Yi's restless, ambitious mind had dazzled the 2,000-year-old world of Chinese acrobatics with new ideas. In San Francisco he took on the challenge of getting a bunch of creative, colorful and not-so-young circus performers up to international standards in pole climbing, hoop-diving, teeterboard, tumbling and other staples of the art.

When I joined the Pickles in 1991, Lu Yi had learned a lot of English and was training some promising youngsters along with the professional company. Over the next seven years, he worked with director/choreographer Tandy Beal to help Diane "Pino" Wasnak and me create over a dozen acrobatic clown acts.

One day, when we were on tour with the Pickles and sharing a room in Cincinnati, Lu Yi told me about sitting in a hotel in Budapest with the rest of his elite Chinese acrobatic troupe, waiting to perform. It was 1956 and they were on a four-month tour of Romania, East Germany, Poland and Hungary. The acrobats weren't told anything about politics or street demonstrations or tanks, Lu Yi said; they just knew that they couldn't leave the hotel, the shades were always drawn and, every day, there was less and less food.

Another time, in Nanjing, we drove past a big, overgrown field beside a freeway. Lu Yi mentioned that this was the spot were he thought up his most famous act — an acrobat standing on a bench balanced on Lu Yi's head while both performers spin plates on sticks, three in each hand. The top acrobat bends backwards so far that she picks an artificial rose with her teeth from a holder below the level of the bench.

Lu Yi had been sent to work in this field alongside the farmers after one of his trips abroad to ensure that he resisted elitist tendencies and stayed connected to the less privileged mass of workers. This gave him plenty of time to daydream new acrobatic moves.

The youngsters Lu Yi trained are now some of the top circus performers in North America, combining Chinese acrobatics with American panache. His latest adventures include training both the American and Japanese Olympic synchronized swimming teams in underwater acrobatics.

CHAPTER TWELVE

COMMEDIA DELL'ARTE
The Clown Conservatory

WE ARE SITTING PRACTICALLY in each other's laps today, trying to stay warm as the wind whips heavy rain against the windows. The heater is broken. The Director, wearing a colorful new Italian sweater, sits down with us and, in a quiet voice, talks about his trip. He finishes with, "So Dominico didn't fire me but I'm not sure why." We are all quiet. I am torn between hating Dominico for being such a jerk to my Director and embarrassed for the Director. The rain eases up for a moment and the Director slowly gets to his feet. "It is not easy being a student. It might be even harder when you are also a teacher. Thinking about all of you, of the risks you take every day and the humility you bring to your work, that saved me from being an arrogant, know-it-all American. You may have saved me my gig. Thank you."

I look over at Ronni, who is wiping her cheek with the back of her hand. Starlight rushes past me to engulf the Director in a gauzy, tie-dyed hug. I try not to giggle at the startled look on the Director's face. The rain suddenly tattoos the windows as we all get up, hugging and giving each other high-fives.

The Director has extracted himself from Starlight's embrace and is now standing by the table, which is again covered with a paisley cloth. "Speaking of Italy, didn't you meet Il Dottore right before I left for Europe?" With one smooth move, he again reveals the Commedia dell'arte masks. They are just begging to be worn but, again, not yet. We first need to learn how to use our bodies to support the masks.

We start by walking randomly around the room, sticking one part of our body out in front — our noses, our toes, our chests. The Director calls out a "chest lead" and it is amazing to see my classmates transform into a roomful of arrogant twits. The Director keeps reminding us to stay small and be exact: "Only put your lead out a little bit, the minimum necessary to change your silhouette. If you are leading with your sternum, make sure it is not your belly button or your clavicle."

Remembering that my sternum is the bottom of my rib cage and my clavicle is my shoulder girdle takes all my focus for a moment.

"Now that you have some precision, you can exaggerate. As you walk, push your lead forward and notice how your body adjusts. If the rhythm of your footsteps changes, exaggerate that, if your arms or head or hips move differently, exaggerate that. Don't start with your minds; let your bodies have their say first."

After a few moments, I am sweating and aching like I do in acrobatics class. The Director calls a break to demonstrate. He walks around the room with his knees leading ever so slightly; then he exaggerates it. "I notice my arms swinging more and my steps getting longer. My head is pushing forward." He exaggerates each swing, step and push as he says it. "The Italian word *maschera* means "mask," which is a main feature of many Commedia characters." Bari interrupts, "What's the plural of *maschera*?"

We all laugh, including the Director. "For Commedia actors, *maschera* also means one's entire body shaped to support the mask and define the character. My body is now shaped differently than usual; it is a mask."

He is a grotesque with his head thrust forward, arms swinging well past horizontal and his legs eating up space as he strides around the room.

"I am now an abstract creature, strange but not yet a character. To create a complete character, I invite my head and heart, my internal self, to join my body, my external self.

"Adding my brain, I notice the rhythm of my footfall, I think of an animal that might move this way, I can think of a real person or a character in literature who moves like this…" As he talks, the Director almost imperceptibly fills his body. He becomes a different person walking around, a fully formed character.

This character-that-was-our-Director starts looking at each of us in turn, reacting either aggressively or submissively as we return his stare. When he looks at me, he brings up his chest in a challenging gesture and, without thinking, my chest puffs out to meet his challenge. He cringes and moves on. I am embarrassingly happy about winning this confrontation.

Our Director is back again, standing in front of us.

"Bringing in my heart means finding my place in the society of this room. You don't go into a room alone and discover yourself or your character; you find your inner life by bouncing off of other people, other characters.

"Commedia grew out of a feudal society, a world where you were born into a caste and stayed there for life. There were servants and masters and this is how the characters are still defined today. In improv class you talk about status. For us moderns, it is important to play with status and caste, find how it affects our hearts and how it may still ring true in our supposedly classless world."

The Director turns away again and when he turns back to face us, he's wearing the phallic-nosed mask I picked up when I first came into class.

"You, Jake!" He puffs out his chest, strides toward me. "You! are! in! my! way! You have angered the great Capitano!" I puff up to meet his challenge and instantly he cringes and scuttles away. "You win. Sorry. I was just…just…" We howl at this reaction.

The mask is off and our Director is back. "You laugh when my status changes, when I am suddenly the opposite of what I was a moment ago. This is called the Mask and the Contramask. Il Capitano is a great character to illustrate this — he is a peacock whose mask is a conquering soldier and his contramask is a complete coward. Thank you, Jake, for standing up to the bully, Il Capitano."

I bow and my classmates applaud sarcastically.

"All of us humans have a big range of behavior, from one extreme to another." The Director holds up his hands as far apart as he can. "In some schools of acting, we are looking for the subtle gradations along this spectrum; in Commedia, we cut out the middle and quickly go from one extreme to the other. This works for comic effect and, somehow, rings true to life."

The Director turns around and, when he's facing us again, he has a fan in his hand.

Swish, the fan opens and, as he brings it up to his face, our director changes — his voice is slightly higher, his neck seems longer and his head is tilted coyly. "You see, I, Isabella, don't need a mask to be me, just a fan." The fan closes and Isabella slaps it against her palm, "Now get back to work! What is your lead?"

We all jump and, starting with a lead, quickly turn our bodies into grotesques that waddle or glide or prance around the room.

Another slap of the fan, "Freeze!" I stop and relax. Isabella snaps, "Keep your body, Jake." I quickly go back into the chest-led creature I was. Isabella coos, "Beautiful, bambino, bella." I feel the fan glide down my arm but stay frozen. "This is your 'zero.'" Now you are frozen action rather than just dead meat, *morta maschera*. You must be alive, in action, even when you are frozen in your zero." I try to be fully alive. The fan smacks my shoulder as Isabella says, "Si, si, ragazzo, now you are alive. Now everyone look at me." We all snap our focus to Isabella. "Perfetto, ragazzi. You are all in zeroes — frozen action, fully alive in your beautiful bodies, throwing focus where it should be, at me, at Isabella."

One final slap of the fan; Isabella turns around and our Director is back. "Now you know about leads, about Mask and Contramask and how to hold a zero. Just one more thing before you get your masks: Each character is based on a different animal. This helps you understand both the movement and the personality of that character. For example Isabella, who you just met, is a swan."

"Now, would half of you please come up and pick out any mask that catches your fancy." Before I can get two steps, Roger, Virginie, Dan and Starlight are holding masks, ready to put them on.

The Director stops them, "Almost everywhere in the world, masks are considered magical." Starlight sighs. The Director nods at her and continues, "If you are like me, cynical and agnostic, this is a good moment to stretch your heart to include spirituality, to embrace the unknowable. Treat your mask with holy respect." Starlight closes her eyes and gently runs a hand over the brow of the Il Dottore mask. Roger tweaks the phallic nose of the Capitano mask that he's chosen; Dan and Virginie quietly examine their masks, Brighella and Pulcinella.

A moment later, the Director signals for my classmates to turn upstage and we see elastic straps getting adjusted under heads of hair. We watch as our classmates, still facing away from us, slowly bend their knees, twist their arms and stick their butts out at odd angles.

"Good. On a scale of 10, you are at a 5; turn it up to a 7." The butts stick way out, elbows and knees stretch to their limits. "Good, good. Hold still. Now slowly turn your masks to look at us without moving your bodies. Isolate your heads."

Giant noses peek over shoulders.

"Now hold your masks still and turn your bodies to us. Isolate your bodies."

Standing in front of us, where our classmates used to be, are strangers.

"Look left!"

Masks snap.

"Look right!"

Snap again.

"Look at us and open your mouths wide!"

We gasp — as their mouths open the masks suddenly come alive. These creatures are living, breathing people, strange and familiar.

A moment later, the masks are off and even Roger looks moved.

By the end of the class, I've played three characters: Pulcinella, a hooked nosed, hunchbacked servant who has two huge appetites — food and sex; Colombina, a scheming maid whose animal is a pigeon; and my favorite, Pantalone, the rich, paranoid miser who moves like a duck.

It's not clowning, but Commedia dell'arte characters are extreme, funny and physical, like clowns. We won't have time to put it all together — the masked characters improvising dialogue and physical business between well-rehearsed lazzi within the structure of a scenario — but even the short scenes we're going to create will give the next audience a taste of our 16th-century Italian ancestors.

Jake's Journal #7, January 16

Big Idea:
- *Commedia characters may be old but they ROCK.*

Why is this important for me?
- *I've never thought of performing with a mask before.*
- *Clown makeup and clown noses are kinds of masks.*
- *Leads, Mask/Contramask, animals, appetites — these tools can me help create any kind of character.*

What I need to rehearse:
- *Mask and contramask for my character, Pantalone — he's the master of the house and then scared shitless someone is trying to steal his money.*
- *The show is in 11 days — need to rehearse all the lazzi: trying to get money bags from Il Dottore, beating up my servant Arlecchino, getting hit by Arlecchino when I'm in the big sack.*
- *Try to juggle the money bags with my mask on.*
- *Work on falling and rolling backward in the mask and costume.*
- *Use mime technique to hold still in a zero and to isolate moving the mask and moving my body.*
- *No dance or acrobatic acts in this next show!!*

Exercises:
- *Head takes with the masks.*
- *Make a physical character by exaggerating that lead, letting my body shape up around it and then bringing in my head and heart.*
- *A zero is frozen action, fully alive and throwing focus; hit zeroes on every entrance and exit.*
- *The mask is sacred (even if I don't believe in sacred).*

Ah-ha Moment:
- *The way the mask changes expressions when the performer is completely committed.*

CHAPTER THIRTEEN

WHEN CHICKENS DON'T FALL
DALLAS, TEXAS
Cirque du Soleil

THE INTERMISSION IS OVER and I am feeling my way through the dark tunnel under the seats to a place where I can peek out at the stage. My big black terrycloth robe with the Cirque du Soleil logo on the back protects me from the gusts of chilly Texas wind that leak into the tent. I start the second half of *Corteo* in a Harlequin costume, a 19th-century version of Arlecchino. This costume is much lighter than the funeral suit I wear in the first half, so on cold days I wear the robe.

The big aerial act is going flawlessly, as usual, with small Russian flyers getting caught by large Ukrainian porters after spinning and flipping through the air. Two ushers, young women identically dressed in tight black jeans and tight black Cirque du Soleil sweatshirts, stand a few feet away from me arguing over which of the porters has the hottest body. The ushers are local hires, just in for our run here in Dallas, so they aren't used to spending their workdays amongst the Buff and Beautiful. The men in the aerial act perform bare-chested, so the ushers have a lot of erotic evidence to discuss.

As the act ends and the acrobats bow, I hand my robe to one of the ushers and walk into the audience. My first job is to create a distraction so the stage crew can strike the safety net. Vittorio, a 6 foot, 10 inch Argentinian opera singer, joins me in one spotlight and the Ringmaster, a rotund whistler from Nebraska, is on the other side of the audience in another spotlight. Vittorio and I dance in the aisle to the Ringmaster's whistled rendition of a Verdi melody. Then we all come onto the stage.

I cross to a long table covered with a black sheet hiding the glass harmonica, 17 wine glasses carefully filled with different amounts of water. I pull off the sheet and there is blood on the table.

Vittorio and I look at each other and make a silent pact to keep the act going. We both try not to touch the blood. My mind races from one horrible explanation to another as I run my fingers over the rims to make the eerie sounds of the glass harmonica. The Ringmaster, who is oblivious to the blood on the table, tunes up with the violin player.

I come center stage, on cue, and announce, "Il concerto!" And nothing happens. "Il concerto!" is Freddo's cue to drop a stuffed rubber chicken from the top of the tent onto my head. But there is no chicken.

> Blood on the table and no chicken on my head — this is bad.
> Is Freddo dead? Did he fall from his perch at intermission
> and bleed out on our table? How did he manage not to break
> the glasses? Where is the body?

I force myself back to the moment, scrambling to think of what my next move should be if Freddo is dead, leaving no one to drop a chicken on my head.

> I should have thought about this *before* the show, not during.
> I'm not ready for a golden mistake.

I finally figure out that my next move is to cue the bandleader and then play the glass harmonica. I give the cue and start to cross to the table when, bang, a chicken hits me on the head.

> Freddo is alive!

A few kids in the audience laugh loudly at the chicken, which throws off my timing so I cue the band again, clumsily, and somehow that gets a nice chuckle. A few minutes later, when the two-person horse enters, the same kids really howl, which gets us all back on track.

When the scene is finally finished, I race offstage to report the blood but I stop at the Tapis Rouge. One of the stagehands is sitting on the couch strapping a large bandage to his right arm. He had cut himself on the safety rigging and hadn't noticed that he was bleeding until after he had set our table on stage.

Mystery solved.

On the shuttle back to the hotel after the show, I'm still thinking about how to avoid standing in front of 2,800 people waiting for a chicken to drop on my head. I talk with my students about looking for golden mistakes but this was a different kind of mistake, an omission, something that you are expecting to happen that doesn't happen. Of course, the audience doesn't know what is supposed to happen so the approach here needs to be different than a visible mistake like, say, dropping a juggling ball.

To prepare for this no-chicken moment, I should have rehearsed the scene without the cue. How would the scene go if the chicken didn't hit my head, without the interruption?

This idea comes from the world of magic — magicians learn to sell sleight-of-hand tricks, like making a coin disappear, by practicing the move without the coin disappearing. How do I move if there is no sleight, if the coin ends up in the hand the audience thinks it's in? That is the natural flow of the hand-off; the moment the coin is palmed, the sleight, is the interruption. Practicing without the sleight allows the magician to replicate the exact moves that make us think the coin is in one hand when it is actually palmed in the other.

For clowns, this kind of practice helps in two ways: we seem genuinely interrupted by the chicken on the nights when everything goes as planned, and it lets us continue unfazed if the chicken doesn't fall on cue. We want planned interruptions to seem like golden mistakes and we want to have genuinely missed cues go unnoticed.

I finish my anchovy dip, fall into bed without checking my email and dream of bloody chickens dancing to the eerie sounds of the glass harmonica.

I'm up early and off to the airport to pick up my wife, the boys and my mother-in-law, who is nearly 90 and in such good shape she could do a show or two if we needed backup. The family is here for my fiftieth birthday party on Monday night. My wife's bringing a stack of bright yellow and red fliers, inviting the *Corteo* folks to the party in French, Russian and English. Friends and family will start pouring in soon, in time for the Sunday matinee. The box office gave them all a discount and Erik, the head of concessions, promises anyone free popcorn if they say the magic words "Birthday Clown."

In the Artistic Tent, the boys head straight for the trampoline while my wife hands out fliers and introduces the cast to her mother. Soon my mother-in-law is sitting in the Tapis Rouge giving advice on life to the former captains of the Canadian and Brazilian women's Olympic gymnastics teams.

The next two days are a swirl of hugs, food and presents interrupted by performances. Seventy-five friends and family come backstage after the Sunday matinee, escorted by our head of security, a man about my age who looks like a cowboy and sounds like Al Pacino. He can't stop laughing. "Seventy-five guests, man, that is some kind of record. And they all paid! When this clown thing goes south, you should go into marketing."

Luckily some cousins are celebrating their fortieth wedding anniversary across town so I get everyone out of the Artistic Tent in time to warm up for the night show. When I arrive at the hotel about 10:30 pm, the kids are all running around the lobby in their PJs while the adults are drinking wine and swapping stories. I plop down in an overstuffed chair in the middle of it all and my younger son plops down in my lap, followed by my nieces, and everyone tells me their favorite parts of the show.

The invitations work — my birthday party looks and sounds like the United Nations if the General Assembly featured a dog act, a whistler and great food. In the buffet line, my uncle offers advice to Polish acrobats on the right way to dress their mashed potatoes, while the bandleader teaches a table of octogenarians how to make music with little bird whistles half filled with water. Vittorio stops my younger son from pouring a tenth sugar packet into his iced tea and my former clown partner gets her dog to jump over seven kids on their hands and knees.

Sometimes my worlds magically meld together.

SPOTLIGHT:
Z Smith

From a back-row seat in the old Stage Werx, a tiny basement theater near Union Square, I witnessed Z Smith transform. Z was riding a tricycle around the stage in the opening moments of Circus Finelli's new show and everything she did felt inevitable and surprising. I was in the presence of a clown, a clown who delighted us, who was completely in tune with everything around her and seemed to be unable to make a false move.

Z had come to The Clown Conservatory with some good acting training under her belt and the experience of starting a small theater company that had toured western Massachusetts on bicycles. In her second year, Z teamed up with four of her classmates to form the all-female clown troupe Circus Finelli. They had success early, performing in Europe and building a strong fan base in the San Fracisco Bay Area. But not long after the Stage Werx show, Z's mother got sick and Z moved back East to be with her. Circus Finelli continued without her as Z realized that her mother might need help for years, not months.

Eventually Z started to miss performing and needed to make money without going too far from her mother's house. So, somewhat reluctantly, she took a gig at a child's birthday party. She had been thinking of developing a solo show so she decided that performing at this party was research. It went well, the family recommended her to their friends, and one party led to the next. Soon Z Smith had a thriving business based on her own unique approach to children's parties. She was making a living, growing as an artist and taking care of her mom.

Performing at children's birthday parties is looked down on by many other professional clowns, even though party clowns are often the first live performers a child encounters. That child will remember a good clown, or a particularly bad one, for life. In addition, children's parties are unique — they are the only time that most American families invite a professional artist into their home. It takes serious skills to keep a gaggle of sugar-soaked 5-year-olds engaged and, like Z, a party clown can make a good living while controlling her art, her business and her travel schedule.

CHAPTER FOURTEEN

YOU CAN'T PLAY THAT HERE
Clown Conservatory

"WELCOME, LADIES AND GENTLEMEN. Thank you for coming to our show. We have a whole world of clown history for you tonight."

The theater is almost full for this show, our fourth, and we are ready to rock their world. Gone are the early days of slapdash acts done in sweatpants and tee shirts. We are way past trotting out our basic routines like Grapefruit and we've moved forward a few hundred years from the 16th-century masks of Commedia dell'arte. This show is classic European clowning or, to be exact, classic 19th-century European clowning done in 21st-century style.

Huddled behind real theatrical flats, set up on the stage proper this time, my classmates and I look like a Degas circus painting (if Degas had been more interested in clowns than showgirls and horses). There are White clowns in elegant costumes wearing full whiteface makeup with red ears. They are standing next to their Auguste partners in baggy pants, oversized shoes and wide, white mouths. The Ringmasters in their tuxedos stand farther upstage, away from our clown alley.

We had been working for weeks with our French Master, learning half a dozen Clown Entrées. The canon of European clowning includes about 100 of these short clown plays. Some take a few minutes to perform, like "The Dollar Bill." Others are one-act plays, complete with scenes and political resonance, like "Pea Soup," an entrée made popular during the food shortages of World War II. Unlike plays, or Commedia dell'arte, European clown entrées usually only have two or three characters — the White Clown, the Auguste and an authority figure, the Ringmaster.

At the end of our first week working with classic clown entrées, our makeup teacher, who was one of the first women clowns to graduate from Ringling Bros. Clown College, taught us how to put on full white-face. I sat next to Dan as we stared into a wide, cracked mirror smearing thick white grease paint onto our faces. I had to laugh at how ugly I looked with my large nose and dark eyebrows whitewashed. Dan was silent and, when I peeked at him in the mirror, I saw his dark brown skin blotched with white.

"I feel like my ancestors are looking down on me with shame."

I turned to him, "What, what's the shame?"

"No shame for you, Jake, but I'm not you. I'm a black man trying to turn my skin white. This is not my tradition. I'm from another world."

I was silent. It hit me that Dan, our only African-American student, was suddenly thrown into a maelstrom of history, race, politics and even shame by the simple act of applying white makeup. Whiteface. Black face.

I tried to imagine myself putting on the makeup of another tradition — the heavy black and white patches of a Hopi clown or the multicolored dots of an Indian Bhand. As strange as that would be, I wouldn't have the shadow of 400 years of slavery, and the theatrical styles that came out of that horror, that hung over Dan's makeup session.

Dan did put on full whiteface, although he took it off the moment class was over and was upset for days. By the time we got to dress rehearsal, he had found an Auguste makeup, one that features more reds and blacks with only a few small areas of white.

Back in our theater, the Director continues his introduction, "Although the show today is steeped in history, we are not in a museum and this is not a reenactment. A clown's job is to entertain this group of people — you, our audience — right here, right now. So the Clown Conservatory students have taken these classic routines and added their own twists."

The first act begins, a variation on "You Can't Play That Here" but done with a bong and retitled "You Can't Smoke That Here." A modern take on an old gag. Last week we were sure that the Director was going to cut this entrée since we always have kids in the audience. But he let it go, saying, "You have to make this material your own, you have to take risks." He also allowed two bawdy versions of "Somnambulist

Kleptomaniac," an all-male and an all-female version. "Somnambulist Kleptomaniac" is an entrée that has sex built into the scheme of the gag — the ending implies that two clowns are going backstage to consummate an adulterous affair. It wasn't much of a stretch to make these gags truly raunchy.

Because I tweaked my knee doing a dive roll off of a mini-trampoline in acrobatics class two weeks ago, I'm playing a second Auguste, the husband of the White Clown, Roger, in the all-male "Somnambulist." It's a role that only requires sleepwalking on stage three times, stealing first a hat and then a scarf from Dan, the first Auguste. Each time I exit with my stolen item, Roger tells Dan, "Don't worry, I'll return it in the morning." The third time I start to exit with Dan. When the White clown stops us, the first Auguste says, "Don't worry, I'll return him in the morning." Cue music.

I've been hobbling to my classes, doing extra headstands (no pressure on the knee) and sitting down whenever my classmates start moving around. Having such a small role in this show is driving me crazy. I keep telling myself to be patient and everything will be back on track as soon as the knee heals.

The show starts. Bari, an Auguste in a huge dreadlock wig carrying an equally huge bong, climbs into the ring to start "You Can't Smoke That Here." She takes a toke and the Director bolts out of his chair in the front row and heads for the door. He is a fanatic about respecting the "magic of performance," forbidding us to so much as sneeze when our classmates are on stage. Something is seriously wrong.

When the Director opens the door just wide enough to slip out, I see that the hallway is packed with children craning their necks to see in. The French-American day school down the street has decided to take a field trip to see our show today. The Director's bulk fills the door, blocking their view. Bari keeps on smoking the bong, Virginie enters as the White Clown, dressed in a black leather jumpsuit. "You can't smoke that here!" "I can't smoke this here?" "Right, you can't smoke that here." "Cool, mon." Virginie exits, Bari moves her bong to the other side of the stage and takes another toke.

"You Can't Smoke That Here" gets a huge ovation, the smoke clears and the Director sits down, having successfully saved a couple of dozen bilingual children from clown corruption.

The show continues with an entrée called "The Dollar Bill" in which the Auguste, Dan on his unicycle, comes out looking for his lost dollar bill. The White Clown, Anita in a leotard, tutu and oversized toe shoes, joins him and tries to help. After they both search for the bill in the audience, the White Clown asks:

"Where did you last see your dollar bill?"

"In the dressing room, backstage."

"Well then why are we looking out here in the ring?"

"Because it is dark backstage and there is plenty of light out here."

Cue music as Anita chases Dan offstage.

Most of the entrées are like this, with a simple structure and a corny ending. Clown entrées are not Shakespeare. They can fail miserably, as our French Master says, "leaving ze stink of ze dead clown." It is our job to fill them with life and joy and well-made physical gags, updated versions of Commedia lazzi.

There is another version of "You Can't Play That Here," this time with an accordion instead of a bong, plus the two versions of "Somnambulist Kleptomaniac." If the audience realizes they are seeing the same entrées over again, they clearly don't mind — the routines look very different from each other even though we carefully stick to the scheme of the gag.

The grand finale is an updated version of "Pea Soup," a complicated entrée that involves an Auguste inviting the Ringmaster over for a dinner of beef bourguignon. Ronni, looking really good in a classic bolero jacket, is the White Clown. She is thrilled to have a chance to show off for the boss until the Auguste, Starlight, tells her that the Ringmaster is coming in 15 minutes.

Panic!

"You idiot, beef bourguignon takes three days to make, even if we could afford the ingredients. All we have is a pot of pea soup."

The White Clown quickly hatches a plan for the Auguste to pretend to spill the beef bourguignon in the kitchen and then offer the Ringmaster pea soup instead. The next part of the entrée involves the White Clown and the Auguste rehearsing this ruse, which is a disaster because the Auguste doesn't understand the plan or even the concept of rehearsing. When things are at the peak of chaos, the Ringmaster arrives.

In our version, Dan plays the Ringmaster as Barack Obama, flying onstage with a round-off back handspring. In his suit, tie and stage makeup, he is a ringer for the president and gets a show-stopping round of applause when he lands. After some more business, we hear a huge crash offstage in the "kitchen" and Obama looks shocked while the White Clown gives an aside to the audience, "Maybe the plan will work after all." In runs the Auguste, distraught.

The White says slowly, giving the Auguste her cue, "What happened, did you spill the beef bourguignon?"

"No, I spilled the pea soup."

Cue music and the White Clown chases Auguste offstage while Ringmaster Obama chases the White Clown. The audience stands and cheers. I hobble out for the full-cast bow and then sit off to the side as my classmates hug their friends, pack up their props and get out of costume. I'm basically in street clothes already so I just sit with my leg up on a chair.

The Director eventually shoos the stragglers out of the theater and gathers the class. They stand in a circle around me and my propped-up leg. The Director starts, as he always does, by asking what moments in the show really worked. My name doesn't come up.

The post-show debrief is over and I'm hobbling up the stairs to the streetcar stop. Charlotte, a shy trapeze student who comes to all of our shows, offers to help me. "Thanks, I got it." "Oh, OK. How'd you hurt your knee?" She has a hint of an accent, somewhere in the South. "Mini-tramp." We're starting up the second flight and I stumble. "Maybe I could use a little help." Charlotte is about my height and thin like most of the aerialists. She puts her arm around my waist and I put my arm over her shoulders, under her mass of curly black hair. She is seriously strong. We chat at the streetcar stop — she's from Atlanta, knew Dan back home, competitive gymnastics through high school, fell in love with trapeze at college in Florida.

A couple of streetcars go by and we ignore them. Eventually I ask Charlotte if she's hungry. She is, and we go to the crêpe place a couple of blocks away for dinner.

Jake's Journal #8, March 12

Big Ideas:

- *Found this book review in the paper: "Amy Bloom's new novel could be called formulaic. Bloom isn't fighting traditional form but her execution is exquisite." Clown Entrées are moldy old formulas. Doing them well is all about exquisite execution.*

Why is it important to me?

- *Entrées are longer than routines like Grapefruit; they are really short plays.*
- *Actors have Shakespeare and Tennessee Williams but clowns have Dollar Bill and Pea Soup.*
- *More material, already time-tested and ready to go!*
- *Clown Entrées = templates for clowns to pour their own personalities into.*
- *An audience can watch different clowns do the exact same entrée a few times in one show and not get bored.*

Exercises:

- *Learn more of these entrées like actors learn monologues.*
- *Bring my own point of view, my own sense of humor to these entrées.*
- *Update entrées, make them edgy and even political.*
- *Keep doing the exercises the physical therapist gave me for my knee.*

Clowns in Community project:

- *Get a badge at S.F. General Hospital so we can start doing hospital clowning. I hope I don't need to be a clown IN the hospital getting my knee operated on :O(*
- *Find stories to bring in to class for the next show, storytelling.*

Ah-ha Moment:

- *When the audience went crazy for Ringmaster Obama. It was like the Colbert Report or the Daily Show, only live and with clowns.*

CHAPTER FIFTEEN

ICHABOD CRANE
LOS ANGELES, CALIFORNIA.
Cirque du Soleil

WHEN I RETURN TO CIRQUE DU SOLEIL, the big blue-and-yellow tent is in Los Angeles. My boss's boss and two more layers of bosses are slated to attend the premiere tomorrow night, along with the owner Guy Laliberté. After the show, I will join some of the top circus brass onstage as part of a question-and-answer session for Cirque Club members. We are celebrating the 20th anniversary of "Cirque du Soleil in the City of Angels." Then it's off to the after-party at the Forum, a former basketball arena next door to our site. The P.R. folks have printed a guide for us with names, pictures and credits of the famous people we may meet, in alphabetical order by first name, from Eva Longoria to Mariel Hemingway to Wolfgang Puck.

The elevated level of glamour and my semi-star status makes me a bit uncomfortable. Back in Dallas, one of the local box office folks came up to me on the back lot and said, "You're the star, man, and you're walking around saying 'hi' to everyone like you're just folks." He meant it as a compliment and I took it that way. I enjoy being friendly with everyone and I get a thrill when my friendship is seen as special because of my job. I like being the down-to-earth kind of star. But here in L.A., the star game is played with a lot more skill and danger than in Dallas and I'm also quite sure I don't have the stomach for even the beginner's track.

The new *Corteo* program came today, only three months after the office folks said it would arrive. The wait was worth it — it is beautifully done, the size of a book and there are pictures of me, looking much better than I do in life, on every other page. It makes me happy that

Cirque du Soleil now recognizes me as a key performer and it is nice to have my image go home with the purchasing public.

The new program came at a good time, right after an online review criticized my voice. I've worked hard for years to improve my voice, which was a liability early in my career. The review sent me into the spiral of doubt that artists sometimes fall into, asking myself, "Does my voice really suck? Will my bosses hate what they see and hear at the premiere? Is this my last performing gig?" Seeing the new program slowed the fall.

Email from Jamarr Woodruff (Clown Conservatory class of '05):

"Wow, the big opening in L.A. Yes, L.A. is a strange creature. I don't know much about her, but I know some. I feel your anxiety, because you never know who will be watching you. It will probably be someone who you have admired from a distance.

I have had the pleasure of this during my time here at Ringling Bros. Mark Oliver Gebel praised me on my dancing prowess, I have entertained William Shatner, Sarah Jessica Parker, Kobe Bryant and Scottie Pippen just to name a few. The most memorable moment was meeting Stevie Wonder. He was gracious and we talked and talked. I actually had to excuse myself from him to go retrieve some friends from the seats. There is a floating chance I might meet Barack Obama this weekend.

All I have to say is just be yourself, because they are just people like you."

The tent is packed for the premiere and the cast is jazzed. At intermission, one of the veterans gives us the scoop on the owner: "If he comes backstage and chats with us, all is good; if he takes the Artistic Director into his trailer for a private talk, we should all start looking for new jobs."

The audience files out of the tent after a standing ovation; we are all backstage giving high-fives and big hugs. A man in his 40s with a shaved head wearing designer jeans and a well-fitted tee shirt walks into the Artistic Tent. The whole cast, still in costume and makeup, forms a circle as Guy Laliberté offers a few congratulatory words in English with a soft Québécois accent. Then he mumbles something about getting ready for the Q&A and slips off. I think, "Guy is shy. He's one of the richest men in Canada and he still gets self-conscious talking to his employees after a show."

I get out of makeup, into a suit and back onstage to talk with some of the folks who just gave me a standing ovation. The Cirque Club members ask Guy about his artistic inspirations, themes of future shows and his planned trip into space on a Russian rocket. I get one question: "What is it like to work with so many Olympic athletes?" The whole thing takes less than a half hour and I leave the stage deflated. Maybe I need the star treatment more than I want to admit. Cirque du Soleil has always been careful to make the star of every show Cirque du Soleil. Performers are interchangeable. *Corteo* is scheduled to tour for over a decade so after Antonio and I leave, someone else will play the Dead Clown, the leading role, but Cirque du Soleil will always be the star.

On the way to the party, I call my wife to tell her about the show and the standing ovation. She says, "Great. Glad to hear it went well. I made appointments for both boys to go to the dentist next time you're home." We talk about teeth and plumbing and other family logistics for a few minutes until my phone beeps with a call from a student, Jake, who has been depressed lately. I tell my wife I'll call her right back and talk to Jake, who's thinking of taking a week off to go home to New Jersey to heal his knee. Missing a week of school is not an option and I talk him into staying. When I call my wife again, she's furious, "Don't ever hang up on me to talk with a student. You're in love with your school and your show." I'm surprised, make lots of apologetic sounds and we hang up pretty quickly.

It occurs to me that teeth and plumbing and packing lunches before going to work must feel like a trap to my wife. She probably sees my world as opening nights with beautiful young aerialists and my picture in the program. This is so obvious but most of the time I only feel tired and overworked, not glamorous, so I don't understand why she gets mad.

Julie Newmar, who played the original Cat-Woman, is one of the only stars I recognize at the after-party. She visited The Clown Conservatory once. In the car driving her to the school, she turned and said, "This is a professional visit, right, not a fan thing? I want to talk with your students as professionals." When I agreed, she visibly relaxed and then charmed all of us with advice like, "Sew your own costumes. I took that Cat-Woman costume home the night before we shot the first episode and took it in in all the right places. My mother taught me how to use my curves."

I alternate between sitting with Julie and her entourage and eating hors d'oeuvres with my cast-mates before slipping out early. I'm happy I still have a job and I'm ready to get some sleep before digging into a long run of shows here in the City of Angels. And I need to call home early in the morning, before the kids go to school.

Along with the beautiful new *Corteo* program, new jugglers have arrived to learn the show. The current jugglers are from Russia, three brothers and a sister. They do an act that their parents polished for years before passing it down a generation, a 40-year-old juggling routine performed by twenty-somethings. The audience loves it. I do, too.

But the Russians are leaving and four teenagers from the Ukraine are here to take their place. Watching the newbies rehearse, I can see that they are all solo jugglers who were thrown together for this job. Their routine is not at the level of the current act. The Artistic Director has been rehearsing them hard but the Russian family will continue performing until the young Ukrainians are up to speed. It might be a while.

One of the new jugglers is a lanky, awkward 19-year-old who looks like a schoolboy next to the sleek, buff acrobats. Even with my very limited Russian, I can tell he is being teased relentlessly. In the middle of the Friday night show, watching the Russian family doing their juggling act on the live feed in the Tapis Rouge, I look up to see this young juggler standing in the middle of the Artistic Tent throwing five juggling clubs in a perfect pattern.

The music is playing, the Russian family is performing onstage and the Ukrainian is backstage juggling five clubs. One at a time everyone in the Artistic Tent turns to watch him. The five clubs stay in the air, a blur set to the rhythm of the handles slapping his hands as he catches.

Doing five clubs for a full minute is a feat — I've never made

it for more than 15 seconds — and he's had the clubs in the
air for over five minutes already!

The music stops, the Russian family exits into the Artistic Tent. They glance at the young juggler as they run to their dressing rooms. Once they have passed, the Ukrainian calmly catches the five clubs, turns and walks away. We all exhale.

Saturday afternoon, when I come in to stretch before the first show, I see the Five Club Wonder bouncing on the trampoline. He looks like Ichabod Crane getting thrown from his horse, with elbows flying and butt sticking out at a strange angle. I think, "What are you doing? Yesterday you carefully choreographed some respect and now you look like a fool in front of everyone."

Sure enough, a couple of acrobats sidle over to the trampoline to loudly comment, in English, on his awful technique. Rather than getting pissed or stopping, he asks for some advice on his trampoline technique. This only gets him another round of sarcastic remarks. He bounces on.

Every day for the next week he bounces on the trampoline and every day the same acrobats tease him. But by the next weekend, the Buff and the Beautiful are also giving Ichabod advice, which he immediately takes. Sunday after the final show of the week, as I'm scooting out to catch the first shuttle back to the hotel, there he is, bouncing away. He looks a little less awkward.

It's a week later and the old juggling act is back in Russia, the new jugglers are in the show and backstage the lanky Ukrainian is looking pretty good on the trampoline.

Driving back up Interstate 5, heading home to try to be a better dad and husband, I am still thinking about this young man. He not only knows how to learn, he knows how to create teachers for himself. Among my students, I've seen some brilliant ones falter during the school year because they couldn't park their egos long enough to learn. I've also seen students who come to school without obvious gifts but who eventually flourish because they take it all in, digest the learning, however slowly, and are willing to fail and flail to get good. It has taken me a long, long time to learn what this 19-year-old Ukrainian juggler already knows — seek out teachers, teachers who sometimes don't even know they are teaching you, and listen to them with humility.

SPOTLIGHT:
Yuri Belov

It was 1997 and Ringling Clown College was abuzz about the impending visit of the great Russian clown director Yuri Belov. I stood behind the 50 young clown hopefuls sitting on the tumbling mats that covered the stage, facing the empty seats. A small man in his 60s sat on a folded mat with another man on a mat a few yards to his right. A regal woman was on the other side of him, sitting straight-backed in a chair. The small man spoke in heavily accented English mixed with Russian while the other man, Yuri's translator, tried his best to help us understand. The woman sat and stared; the students listened. I didn't understand much of what Yuri was saying so I assumed that they didn't either. Five minutes before the end of class, the woman lifted her hand and said, "Yura." Yuri stopped, turned and started to apologize profusely for not introducing his wife, Tanya. When he finally did introduce her, quite formally, Tanya purred, "It is too late, Yura. The time has passed."

Since I didn't have classes, I followed Yuri, Tanya and the translator all day, watching the same lesson repeated five times for five groups of polite but confused students. I didn't understand much but, by the next morning, I had figured out Yuri's concepts. The Belovs were gone but the translator, who had seen the students' struggle, gave me permission to re-teach Yuri's lessons. So I spent my day at Clown College teaching Gags and Gimmicks. A gag is a clown routine, an entrée, a mini play; the "scheme of the gag" is the essential spine of a routine that cannot be changed. To create a fully fleshed-out routine from the scheme of a gag, a clown needs to use gimmicks. A gimmick is a tiny moment of clowning that has a specific three-part structure. Yuri says that gimmicks are for clowns what notes are for musicians — a clown is always doing one of three things: starting a gimmick, playing a gimmick or taking a pause between gimmicks. Gimmicks are, for Yuri, the language of clowns.

CHAPTER SIXTEEN

STORIES AND STORIES AND STORIES

Clown Conservatory

OUR CLASSROOM IS SET UP for the evening show but it looks completely different than the proscenium stage we used for the entrée performance over a month ago. We look different, too. Today, the chairs are in a big circle and we're sitting in our street clothes with a few hats and colorful scarves. Some props are strategically placed next to seats.

Unfortunately, I feel the same — rotten. My knee may be healing, as the physical therapist says, but I can't feel it. I'm still going to classes, sitting most of the time watching my classmates get better while I decay. Even my juggling is suffering. And there's the thing with Charlotte. We went out a couple more times after crêpes and it was feeling pretty good. Then I see her at lunch one day with a guy who looks like a linebacker. She introduces him as her acrobatic partner from college. Any idiot could tell he was her boyfriend. We haven't said a word to each other since then.

"The audience will sit in a circle, like we've been doing in class the last few weeks," the Director says. "You get to sit with them and share your stories, just like humans have been doing for thousands of years. Storytelling is as intimate and connected an act as clowning. The relationship between you and your listeners is the art as much as the words and movements and tricks."

A few weeks ago, we'd all brought in favorite children's stories, poems, myths, legends, and even paintings, photos and songs. We also told stories from our lives. I told about the time I taught juggling in high school for P.E. credit. It seemed like the best class ever — hanging out with my friends and juggling instead of doing laps and getting yelled at by a guy with a crew cut and a whistle. But the first few weeks were rough. I didn't have a clue how to teach and the students gave up so quickly I ended up being the one doing the yelling.

We each zeroed in on a story to use in the show, either our own or something from a book, and started rehearsing. Going around the circle, each person would tell their chosen story and then someone else retold the same story from a different point of view. Finally, a third person told the same story from the point of view of an inanimate object. This third telling was a revelation.

Anita originally told her story, in English and her native Spanish, from the point of view of herself as a girl going to una escuela de baile. Ronni then told it from the point of view of her teacher and I retold it from the point of view of her pink tutu. Without thinking about it, I found myself talking about the pain inside the girl wearing me, the fear of the aging ballerina teaching the class and the claustrophobic ambition of the girl's mother. Anita left the room before I had finished but the next day she told me she had rewritten her story and it was better.

Next we added music, then circus skills like juggling or magic or even acrobatics, and dance. I added everything that my knee would allow, perhaps a little more than I should have. We then told our stories without words using our mime skills. When the Director allowed us to bring back the words, we found that we needed fewer of them. Finally, the Director insisted that each story have a narrator and at least one character with its own distinct voice and body.

The Director stands up and says, "The audience will join us in an hour. Take this time to prepare. Remember, telling a story is a dialogue, even if you are the only one speaking. Your listeners will see and feel the images in your story while conjuring up stories of their own. When Anita talks about putting on a tutu for the first time, the room will fill with thoughts of dance classes, tutus and first times; when Dan starts his Aesop's fable, some audience members will think of other fables, some will be back on their grandpa's lap hearing "The Fox and the Crow" for the first time and some will think of foxes and some will think of crows."

I find an empty corner of the theater and start to tell my story to the wall, an excerpt from my favorite kid's book "The Phantom Tollbooth." Yesterday the Director told me I was the last story, the closing act. I don't know if he's just trying to make me feel better after my pathetic role in the clown entrée show but I'm determined to make sure the show ends strong.

In my story, a boy named Milo has to scale the Mountains of Ignorance to rescue the princesses Rhyme and Reason. The Mathemagician is there with a final gift before Milo heads off with his companions, the watchdog Tock and the Humbug pulling up the rear. I get on all fours to play Tock and my knee screams.

I must have screamed, too, because the Director is kneeling over me with his hands on my leg. The frustrations of the last month come flying out of my mouth.

It isn't pretty.

My classmates pause and then tentatively go back to their rehearsing. My knee hurts too much to feel any shame. The Director helps me stand and we walk outside together. I'm glad to get away from the others, to get out of the theater and into the cold San Francisco fog. My knee can hold my weight, luckily, but I am crying. I can't even tell a simple story without falling apart! How can I get a job in a circus if I end up cursing my knee at every rehearsal? Forget doing acrobatics or dancing or even mime. I'm totally screwed.

"Jake, you've had a rough time lately. Why don't you take a few minutes for yourself before the show." His voice brings me back to the cement steps in front of the school.

"OK."

"Want to go over to Kezar?"

"OK."

The Director helps me down the stairs and steers me toward the high school football field across from The Clown Conservatory. When we get to the bleachers, he says, "I have to get back to the class. See you at show time."

I sit on the very top tier and stare at the metal slat below my feet and then the next slat and the next, on down the bleachers. My knee throbs. I want to go back and rehearse with my classmates but I don't move. I try to think through my story but I can't.

It's been a while and I know I need to get back. I imagine what would happen if I just stayed sitting in the bleachers.

A few minutes later I find myself on the sidewalk in front of the school. A couple is hustling up the stairs so I limp along behind them and manage to slip into the theater just as the Director is standing up to begin the show. I see an empty chair with the juggling club that I use as the Mathemagician's staff carefully placed beside it. I sit down gingerly in the chair with my leg stretched in front of me. I feel my classmates staring at me but I don't look up.

Ronni starts telling a Dr. Seuss story. I know she's trying some tough juggling patterns to illustrate the action but my eyes don't leave the floor. I don't applaud at the end and then feel terrible for being a bad friend. Dan's "Fox and Crow" is next. He used the Commedia character Capitano to create the Fox. The audience is eating it up, talking back to the Fox and laughing at his every retort. I sneak a peek at Dan, and Ronni looks at me. I try to smile.

I'm back to looking at the floor as the show goes on: Virginie's French fairy tale is different than the last time I heard it — the nursemaid now sounds like a Nazi and the girl is a dominatrix; Roger is uncharacteristically subtle telling the story of his grandmother's funeral in Taipei, with only one trick, making a dove appear, right at the end; Anita brings the audience to tears with her story of being groomed to be a ballerina.

The magic of a story circle is lifting my mood and the short bursts of music and circus skills are pulling my eyes up from the floor. I manage to applaud and even smile.

It just got quiet. Someone missed their cue. I look around and my classmates are all looking at me. I look down and see the juggling club. It's my turn.

I look at the Director, trying to will him to stand up and thank the crowd for coming. Instead, he nods at me.

The room gets silent. I look up, take a breath and the story starts to come out of my mouth in a soft monotone that sounds like someone I don't know. I hear the voice mention the Mathemagician but my hand doesn't pick up the staff. The voice drones on.

I take a breath and the room is silent in a way I have only heard at funerals. I'm dying. My story is dying. I've killed the show. I look down and the voice starts again, finishing the story with princesses saved and Milo back in his once-boring room. "…I would like to make another trip but I really don't know when I'll have time. There's just so much to do right here." Silence. I add, "The end." More silence.

Finally the audience applauds. A lot. I look up to see Ronni wiping her eyes and the Director standing with the rest of the audience, smiling at me. What happened? I completely messed up my story — no juggling, no characters, no inflection, nothing. Ronni comes over and gives me a hug. "You were great, Jake. I was worried." Other classmates come over and hug me. I just sit there.

The audience isn't leaving. Some come up to tell me they liked my story; one woman in her 40s tells me that her father used to read "Phantom Tollbooth" to her every night. She says that for months she couldn't get to sleep without hearing a few pages. I listen and nod, shy and a little in shock. I want to apologize for not telling it very well but can't find the words.

It's been a while and the audience has settled in around the room, sitting in pairs and small groups telling their own stories, pulling my classmates into their story circles from time to time. I see a guy with blond dreadlocks and patched pants giving Dan an animated lecture on Aesop's roots in African culture.

Now the room is down to just us students and the Director. I manage to stand, leaning on Roger. We form our customary post-show circle and listen as the Director starts the debrief. "You have been attracting larger and larger audiences, from our first, thrown together show to the second one that focused on Grapefruit and other simple routines. The Commedia dell'arte show was our first big house and Clown Entrées was even better. And now, on our fifth show, we've hit the Holy Grail — standing room only with a standing O."

Everyone applauds.

"And you all rocked the room. Thank you for your stories. As I listened to you, I was as swept away as any of our guests. I learned a lot from all of you this evening, especially Jake." I look up quickly and see my classmates nodding and smiling. I croak out a sound that might have been, "What?"

"Jake, we were engrossed in both your story and your storytelling. We were rooting for you as much as for Milo, Tock and the Princesses. Everyone was listening for your next word, hoping it would come."

"But I didn't do anything."

"No, you didn't do anything except find a way to come back in here and tell a story. That was enough."

"OK. I'm glad." I can't find any other words to say.

"More than any other, this show blurred the line between performers and audience. You created a very direct, visceral bond between the audience and yourselves, just like good clowning. But storytelling isn't clowning. For you, my clowns, the question to ask yourselves is 'What can I take from tonight to use in my clowning tomorrow?'"

Roger and Starlight quickly raise their hands but the Director stops them.

"Think about that question and let your answers show up in your work. Stories beget stories, so, if you will indulge me, I would like to share a story of my own with you. Jake, your struggle today made me think of Oksana, my favorite performer in *Corteo*…"

Jake's Journal #9, April 27

Really hard time right now. Having trouble even keeping up with my notes. Fucking knee is never going to heal, I'm going to have to quit school and go home a failure...I'm trying not to go down that road.

Need to keep focused on learning by watching and listening. This knee has to heal sometime. I'm young and healthy. Maybe there's something broken in there that they can't find, maybe it's more serious than they think and I'm not going to be able to walk soon, much less do a forward roll...here I go again. Focus on my work.

Got to schedule an interview with someone at S.F. General, maybe a patient. Can't even imagine taking the bus all the way down there. But I will, tomorrow or Sunday. Good thing hospitals are open 24/7.

Called mom last night. I told her I have no one to talk to here, I'm really far away from everyone I love, I'm limping around and all these people with perfect bodies are learning amazing things while I become an ugly slug. She didn't say, "See I told you so." She did ask if I wanted to come home. It took me a minute but I said, "No" and I meant it. Just saying out loud that I wanted to be here made me feel a little better. My dad got on the line and told me I was welcome to come to the all-day faculty meeting he has today. I said, "No thanks" and told him about Charlotte's boyfriend showing up. He told me about meeting mom's ex once at a reunion and we laughed. Maybe I should go home.

CHAPTER SEVENTEEN

HELIUM
(THE DIRECTOR'S STORY)
Cirque du Soleil

…OKSANA AND HER HUSBAND MAXIM are from Odessa. They have been circus performers for over three decades. The story goes that Dominico hired them onto *Corteo* after luring them away from a Russian show called the Lilliputian Circus. Oksana and Maxim are both under three feet tall. They did acrobatics and a trained house cat act. Because Cirque du Soleil had branded itself as a no-animal circus, the cats aren't in *Corteo*, but the act that Dominico created for Oksana, called "Helium," is my favorite act of the show.

Helium is a simple routine that contains, in its five minutes, everything that is profound in circus.

For Helium, Oksana has six huge helium balloons attached to her belt so she weighs less than a pound. In the wings I float her up and hold her feet in my hands. On cue I walk to center stage while moving Oksana's feet back and forth so it looks like she's walking five feet above the ground. Then I gently push her and watch as she floats out over the audience. From 20 feet above their heads, Oksana makes quips in Russian and English, her squeaky voice supplying the perfect sound track to the image of a tiny woman floating through the air.

Every time Oksana loses altitude, someone in the crowd catches the bottoms of her feet and gently pushes her back up toward the tent top. They are touching a performer's sole. They are changing gravity. They are creating wonder.

Gravity and wonder — the building blocks of circus.

After a few minutes of floating and catching, I convince someone to push her back to me. Since our stage bisects the audience, I then float Oksana off on the other side. Helium is a well-structured improvisation for one tiny Ukrainian actress, one large American clown and 2,800 spectators.

Structure and improvisation — the tools of every clown.

One cold Dallas day, Maxim arrived at the Artistic Tent alone. He told us that Oksana's father had died suddenly back in Odessa. He said she was very sad but would do the shows, that her family had agreed to delay the funeral until she could fly home on the break in two weeks' time. When Oksana arrived an hour later, she looked even smaller than usual and, for the first time since I'd known her, she didn't talk with anyone. The Artistic Tent was a quieter, sadder place.

But she was brilliant in the show.

One Saturday night, a couple of days before she would get on a plane to Odessa, Oksana had the kind of show that all performers dream of — perfection. The audience was laughing, sighing, hanging on her every move and sound. At the end of Helium, she floated into my right hand and stood there on one foot. Two thousand, eight hundred people were silent in the way you only hear at weddings and bar mitzvahs. After what must have been a full minute, she finally said, "Ciao." Two thousand, eight hundred people exploded with applause. We walked offstage and she was again the grieving daughter of a father, newly dead and 6,000 miles away.

The cliché of the sad clown is just that, a cliché. But Oksana gave me a peek at what real sadness can do for a great clown. Oksana used the power of Lu Yi's "inside clown" when she turned heartbreak into brilliance. The 49 percent tragedy that Carlo Mazzone-Clementi talked about was easy for Oksana to find, and the 51 percent comedy is built into Helium.

When I talk with you about the formula of 51 percent comedy/49 percent tragedy, I hope the tragedy isn't as real as it was for Oksana. But you can tell from the personal stories you've told each other that there is never a shortage of tragedy in our lives, whether it is Anita being pushed to become a ballerina or Roger burying a grandmother thousands of miles from his home.

CHAPTER EIGHTEEN

DANCING WITH DOCTORS

Clown Conservatory

SPRINGTIME BY THE BAY has been a hit or miss kind of thing. This Monday morning is beautiful, even out here in the Sunset District. Most days start out cold and foggy and then change from hour to hour and neighborhood to neighborhood — the Mission is often sunny when the Richmond is socked in. I'm heading to school early for my final one-on-one meeting with the Director. The 7:35 streetcar comes and it's even more crowded than my usual train.

I'm worried about this meeting. It's been a bad couple of months — first my knee, which meant I was pretty much missing in action for the Classic Entrée show, and then my flameout before the storytelling performance.

I manage to bump my way to the middle of the car and wedge myself into the sea of Suits.

The thing with Charlotte didn't help my mental health, either.

We're a couple of miles from downtown and the train is already completely packed.

This meeting is supposed to be about launching into a professional career; the Director probably thinks I'm not ready, that I might never be ready.

My backpack is right in someone's face so I slide it off, slowly, and put it between my feet.

Maybe I'll tell him about the deal with my folks, about needing to get a job or having to go to grad school, and he can help me get some job, like on a ring crew or something, and I can juggle in the pre-show so it would kind of be a performing gig.

We cross 19th Avenue, about 10 stops away, and I start to wiggle my way to the door.

He has to help me since I hurt my knee at school, so it's his responsibility.

Finally I'm out of the double doors and onto Judah Street. 7th Avenue. Walk fast. I don't want to be late.

He's been gone so much on his gig with Cirque, how can he expect us to be ready to "launch"?

Down the hill and up the stairs to the Director's office. I'm only a couple of minutes late. The Director is sitting at a big, well-worn wooden table.

"Sorry I'm late. N Judah, you know..."

"How's your knee?"

I sit down and start to tell him that my knee's doing a lot better but I morph into a rant about how he's been gone so much and it's hurting the school and...

"Jake, I know it hasn't been easy this year. Before you graduate, you'll get a chance to give us feedback on the school. We want it all and we will use the ideas that you and your classmates give us to get better next year. But right now, this meeting is for you. Would you like to hear some thoughts about your work?"

I want to say "no" and leave before he rips me to shreds. I nod.

"The storytelling show was a big turning point, I think. You had so much going on inside that you couldn't use any of your skills and the audience was entranced. If you bring even a little of the heart and soul you had in that moment to your clowning, you will be unstoppable."

I realize he's giving me a compliment but I can't take it in. "I need a job. If I don't get a gig right after graduation I will never perform, but I need to get my knee 100 percent before I audition..."

"Jake, can I tell you a story about the Eskimo-Indian Olympics?"

This is so out of left field that I can't even answer. The Director takes my silence as a "yes."

"In the eighties, I had a gig teaching circus in a Eskimo village on the Yukon River Delta. One day they had an Eskimo-Indian Olympics competition with a group from another village. A brother and sister on the other team were half black, I forget the backstory, and the other kids treated them like shit. I wanted to sit the kids down and tell them not to be that way, but white teachers had been telling Eskimo kids how to be for too long.

"The sister, who was about 13, competed in a game called the Seal Hop. The Seal Hop started with 10 girls lined up on the hardwood floor in push-up position with their hands in fists. On a signal, they started hopping on their toes and knuckles, legs straight, across the gym. When a girl's arms collapsed or the pain from her bleeding knuckles got too much, she was out. The girls all made it back and forth across the gym twice before the first one collapsed. After a few more laps, it was down to the sister and one other girl. They went another lap and, on the turn, the other girl slipped and flopped onto her stomach. The crowd politely applauded the winner. The sister stopped for a moment in the push-up position and then she kept going. Every few yards, she stopped. Then she would start again. The sister went another lap and a half, stood up and walked out of the gym."

I can't find anything to say so I mumble, "Tough girl. Wow."

The Director takes a sip of coffee. "Jake, you've got everything you need to be a pro right now, even with a sore knee. You're tough. You've got the external skills and, after the storytelling show, we've seen your internal skills. The next step is to put it all together. It is time to stop being a student, someone who is learning skills in separate classes. It is time to become a clown. A clown is always learning, of course, but your teachers are now everyone around you. Talk to people, go to shows, play with babies, dance and sing and perform a lot."

"How's playing with babies going to get me a gig with a circus?"

"We'll help you with that part. There's no guarantee but here's my promise — you dig into these last six weeks of school, doing everything you can do without re-injuring your knee. Have your inside clown work with your outside clown, rehearse routines and improvise. Start thinking like a clown, not a student. You do that and we'll make sure you get seen by people who hire good clowns. Deal?"

"Deal!"

"Oh, and stay away from aerialists, at least until you graduate. We need your full attention."

It's Friday, I'm on a patch of grass in front of San Francisco General Hospital wearing a pink hospital gown over bright pink shorts, huge pink hoop earrings, black clown shoes and bare, hairy legs. My knee is wrapped with a tie-dyed Ace bandage, thanks to Starlight. Bari is playing accordion, dressed in a doctor's white coat with her long, skinny legs in tight yellow pants tucked into large green rain boots.

I reach out my hand to invite a passing doctor to dance. He looks up, hesitates, tucks the file he was reading under his arm and takes my hand. Bari segues to something in ¾ time. The doctor and I waltz.

Every person coming out of or going into the hospital stops to dance with me. Everybody. Nobody walks away. EMTs are dancing with me, children are dancing with me, people with walkers and casts and missing limbs are dancing with me. I feel like I am in complete control, completely tuned in.

It's the final day of our Social Circus module. We've spent a lot of time in the last month training with nurses, interviewing patients and waiting for hours to get our volunteer badges. We've learned about hospital hygiene, confidentiality (called HIPAA) and how Child Life Specialists work with sick kids.

Bari has been my partner at the hospital. Our first visit was to the Volunteer Coordinator's office. We walked in, introduced ourselves and the guy started laughing. We weren't even in costume, we just said, "We're students at The Clown Conservatory" and he couldn't stop laughing.

After a good deal of red tape and a few too many trips to S.F. General, Bari and I both got our badges. This meant that we could do our Medical Clown shift, going room to room together playing with patients, families and even the medical staff. Bari brought her accordion and some soap bubbles; I had juggling balls and playing spoons. We both had on white doctors' coats over basic clown costumes — baggy pants, a white shirt and a loose tie. Our makeup was light, just a little around our eyes and mouths, on the request of the Director. He told us to prepare a few short routines and then be ready to follow the patients' lead, even if that meant dropping our clown characters and just chatting with them human-to-human.

On the elevator up to the children's unit, Bari played a soft song for the worried-looking parents of a small baby. They almost managed to smile. On the unit, we found the nurse who trained us. "Just in time. I know a boy who needs some clowns right now." She showed us which room to visit and rushed off in the opposite direction.

The door was closed so we knocked. Getting permission is one of the core concepts of medical clowning, giving the patient the power to say, "Come in" or "Go away." A woman said, "Come in" so we peeked in. A boy around 8 years old was in a bed playing video games. His mom saw us and asked him if he wanted a show. He said "OK" but didn't look up from his game. Bari and I went into the routine we'd rehearsed, a song with juggling. The boy looked up but didn't say anything. We finished and he just lay there with his arms crossed over his chest. I asked if he was a Hollywood director, auditioning a new act. He said, "Yes, I am a Hollywood director. Play me something faster or you will never be in my movies." So Bari played a Cajun dance number while I followed along on spoons. The boy said, "Good. You're in my movie."

Next we went to the playroom, where a young girl wearing a Snow White costume invited us to a very formal sit-down dinner. A boy dressed as an astronaut and a younger boy playing with dinosaurs came over to taste the imaginary food. The kids were completely absorbed and the parents got to sit back and watch them play. No music, no juggling, just following the kids where they wanted to go.

After the playroom, we knocked on a few more doors but everyone said, "No thanks."

On our way out, a nurse got into the elevator with us a few floors below the children's unit. "Are you clowns?" We said yes and she stuck her hand in the door before it closed. "We need clowns. Come on." She took us down the hall to an adult long-term care facility. We spent a half hour juggling and joking around with folks hooked up to big machines, in wheelchairs and with missing legs. When we finally said we had to go, the nurse walked us back to the elevators. "We need you more than the pediatric unit. Most of the kids have families there with them. My patients are all alone — if they have families, most of them have stopped visiting long ago. Adults need clowns."

Our next assignment was to interview someone at the hospital. Back on the adult unit, I met a large African-American woman sitting in a wheelchair wearing a huge pink robe. We're both from New Jersey so we clicked right away. My Jersey accent came back immediately and we got loud. She told me, "I have eight kids, a shattered pelvis from a car accident and I'm on meds for my bipolar episodes." She'd say she was depressed and then, a moment later, we were howling at a joke she cracked or some dance moves she did in the wheelchair.

Back at school, we created characters based on our interviews. I created Pink.

And now I'm dancing in front of the hospital as Pink. I can do no wrong. Everyone is dancing with me and thanking me for being there. "You made my day!" "This hospital needs more clowns."

It's time to go so Bari is packing up her accordion and I'm saying good-bye. Someone yells, "Jake, you son of a bitch, what are you wearing?" I see the real Pink wheeling toward me, screaming. I run up to her screaming, "I'm you, baby. I am you." She gives me a huge hug and I hear Bari's accordion squeeze out the opening strains of "Hernando's Hideaway." Pink and I tango, wheelchair to thigh, with a crowd of suits and scrubs and hospital gowns cheering us on.

Something is changing for me today, something that might be called a clown character. I'm finding a way to be vulnerable and powerful and myself and someone else all at the same time. I went into the hospital hoping to make a few sick kids laugh. Now I realize that this is what the Director meant when he said, "It's time to be a clown, not a student."

Jake's Journal #10, May 11

Big Idea:
- *Everyone in a hospital, old folks and kids, nurses and moms and dads, needs clowns.*

Why is it important to me?
- *I found a character that people love.*
- *Hospitals and sick people aren't as scary to me as they used to be.*
- *Clowns don't have to stay on stage or in the ring.*
- *Maybe there are paid jobs clowning in hospitals. Or old folks homes or refugee camps. Could I get a clown gig that is more than performing?*

Exercise:
- *Interview someone and then try to embody that person (with respect – this is not satire). Create a character like Pink. The Director calls this "Documentary Clowning."*
- *Find unexpected places to show up and perform. Share the love; get some love.*
- *Good thing I didn't give up on dance class — I needed every dance move I have at the hospital.*

Ah-ha Moment:
- *Tango dancing with Pink.*

CHAPTER NINETEEN

CIRQUE DU MONDE
LOS ANGELES, CALIFORNIA.
Cirque du Soleil

THE TRAFFIC ON INTERSTATE 5 SOUTH comes to a complete stop just north of Buttonwillow for no obvious reason. I get out and see a two-lane parking lot stretching to the horizon. Back in my faded gold Toyota, looking out at the flat fields of the Central Valley, I get a tinge of homesickness. Somehow working in Los Angeles, in the same time zone, only six hours from home, makes touring tougher.

When I was home this week I tried to take my 4-year-old on his first long bike ride. The boys and I often go for Saturday breakfast at Jim's, a local diner. We usually bike the mile and a half, my older son in the lead and my younger one in the bike seat behind me. This time we all rode bikes. It was slow, of course, and the 9-year-old kept riding to the corner and then back to us, but the little guy was doing it. About halfway there, it started to drizzle. We kept going until it was really coming down. The boys were going to get pancakes and bacon no matter what, so I put the 4-year-old in the bike seat and draped his bike over my handlebars. We rode in the rain.

Outside of Jim's we shook like dogs, laughing and barking. Breakfast tasted really good and the waitress didn't mind the boys pretending to be pit bulls the whole time. Unfortunately, it was still pouring when we were done and I had to call my wife to come pick us up — so much for giving her the morning off.

My wife is getting tired. When I'm home, I do as many of the chores as I can and we try to find time to be together, just us. We usually don't succeed. I'm always out of rhythm with my family — the kids no longer eat the cheese sandwiches I made for their lunches; I accidentally drove them to the old dentist's office; the book I was reading to them a month ago is already back at the library.

When we first met, my wife wanted to have children, period. I thought having kids would seriously mess up my career. Twenty years of being a "road warrior" had taught me that the way to stay successful in circus and theater is to be ready to go where the work is, any time. But the touring life was starting to feel thin to me — every night we would make audiences happy and then, after the show, they would go home together and we would go back to our hotel rooms to watch HBO. I was ready for more time in one place and ready for a family to spend that time with.

Starting The Clown Conservatory was my way to stop touring and still make a living. Now I'm back on the road and my family is paying for my success. Most of the time I spend with them is on Skype, which my younger son now refuses to do, saying, "If I can't hug you, Daddy, I don't want to see you." My wife and I hardly talk about anything beyond logistics — that takes up all the time we have together and a little more. Trips home only seem to make things colder.

The traffic finally crawls forward and, after about 20 minutes, I see the accident. All that is left on the roadside is a burned-out SUV without a front end or any discernible color. The ambulances have already screamed off to the ER.

Even with the delay, I arrive at our Venice Beach hotel in time for a ride on my Schwinn along the beach path. It is as crowded as New York with the feel of Berkeley back in the day, all baked in SoCal sunshine. A life outdoors, a city outdoors: bathing suits, roller blades, scooters, beach volleyball, street vendors, a fire twirler and mobs of bike riders. Pulling up to Muscle Beach, I see my friend Bob Yerkes, 75 years old with 60 years of circus and movie stunts on his résumé. Bob is in his bathing trunks lying on his back in the sand holding a twenty-something acrobat in a skimpy bikini upside down in a handstand. Welcome to L.A.

A couple days later, we're in the shuttle rushing back to the tent after shooting a segment of the *Tonight Show*. Before we taped our segment this morning, we shot a teaser in the parking lot. Jay Leno pulled up in one of his classic cars, a purple two-door 1930s Fiat, and we did the clown car bit — each of us getting out of the driver's side door, running around off-camera to get back in the passenger door and out the driver's side again. Seeing huge Vittorio squeeze out followed by tiny Oksana cracked up Jay. After we finished, I got to ride around in the Fiat with Jay (my friend, Jay). We talked about cars or, rather, he talked about cars and I asked questions. Welcome to L.A.

We're late for our usual call, 90 minutes before showtime. As I'm signing in on the call sheet in the Artistic Tent, I notice a bright purple sign-up sheet thumbtacked to the bulletin board. It says we are having a Cirque du Monde next Thursday. Cirque du Monde is the charitable arm of Cirque du Soleil. Because the company's first shows were on the streets of the Québec town of Baie-Saint-Paul, they focus their philanthropy on children who are, or have been, on the streets.

For the touring shows like *Corteo*, a Cirque du Monde means tickets to the show plus a backstage event for a social service organization in each city. Here in L.A. we're being asked to sign up to teach 20 kids from a group home next Thursday. They will be coming for an hour of circus training in the Artistic Tent before eating lunch with us in the cook shack and sitting in the "Guy seats" for the matinee.

I write my name at the top of the sheet and get two young aerialists to add their names. The three of us spend the next few days recruiting, which is surprisingly easy given the fact that next Thursday is a two-show day. Adding the Cirque du Monde, it will mean working 12 hours straight for all of us who volunteer.

Thursday morning comes and 17 performers are in the Artistic Tent setting up juggling equipment, the trampoline, an aerial hoop and even a whistling area. Vittorio is testing the 15 pitch pipes he bought for his "Introduction to Singing Opera" booth. The weariness and cynicism that creeps into the backstage of any touring show evaporates as we get ready for these children.

Our Assistant Stage Manager bursts through the tent door. "They're here!"

In walks a group of tough-looking tweens who stand awkwardly at the edge of the tent, not looking at us or at the equipment. My colleagues are just as awkward as the tweens. Everybody stares and fidgets.

I pull out a long silk scarf, make a trick knot and blow on it to make it disappear. I don't look up or call attention to my magic trick, just like I'm practicing. A few of the tweens notice but don't move anything but their eyes. I can feel my colleagues tensing up. A few more times with the same knot — tie, blow, disappear. Now one small boy has abandoned his cool pose and is staring. I tie the knot again and hold it up for him. Without thinking, he blows on it, and I make it disappear. He giggles. "How'd you do that?" I start to show him how to tie the trick knot and the other kids crowd in.

Soon these foster kids are climbing onto the aerial hoop, jumping on the trampoline, whistling, singing and juggling. My colleagues are coaching, coaxing, spotting and laughing. They are alive in a different way than when they are performing; they are taking care of these children, using their skills to heal some hearts, including their own.

SPOTLIGHT:
Everybody's Family Circus

In the mid-1970s, I worked with small community circus called Everybody's Family Circus. One day we were booked to do a show in a high school gym that was repurposed as a boys' juvenile detention center. We walked in dressed in our clown costumes and makeup, loaded down with mats, juggling clubs and a full-body bear costume. Four inmates — teenagers like me, big and dressed in matching orange jumpsuits — were leaning on the stage, smoking cigarettes. They stared at us, made a few nasty jokes and went back to their smoking. My two partners, both women, looked at me; it was my job to get these hoodlums to move so we could set up for our show.

I walked up to the stage, flap-shoes slapping the wooden floor, squeezed in between two of the young men and said, "Gimme a smoke."
"Motherfucker, clowns don't smoke."
I didn't but I said, "This one does. Now give me a cigarette." He does. I say, "Gotta light?"
Another guy gives me his cigarette, saying, "Go ahead, turkey fuck mine."
I take a long drag, lighting up off the end of the inmate's cigarette, then hand the guy back his smoke and ask, "You guys have to come to this show or is it voluntary?"
"Gotta, that's the rules."

I keep asking questions while my partners lay down the mats and set up the equipment. When my juggling clubs accidently fall out of a bag, one of the inmates asks, "You throw those things?"

"Yeah."
"Bullshit. Prove it."

I throw a few tricks and soon they're learning to juggle, cigarettes carefully extinguished and stashed in jumpsuit pockets for after the show.

CHAPTER TWENTY

GETTING SCREWED

Clown Conservatory

THE DIRECTOR WALKS INTO THE BAR wearing a tailored tan suit over a fuchsia button-down, a far cry from the sweatpants and polo shirts he usually sports. Roger starts teasing him about going all L.A. on us. The Director orders a bottle of Anchor Steam, "a San Francisco beer, brewed a couple of miles from right here."

The whole class is seated around a long wooden table upstairs at the Thirsty Bear in the SoMa district of San Francisco, sharing some drinks on a Friday evening. The Director holds up his bottle. "To all of you." We raise our glasses and drink. Then the Director adds, "Tell me, when you think of the word 'business', what comes to mind?"

Roger slams down his single malt; a few precious drops fly onto his patchwork vest. "Oh, no, let's just have fun. Please."

"We can do both — have fun and talk business." The Director smiles as if this were the most delicious pairing possible. "We are almost at the end of the year and we haven't even touched business. Not good. To business!" Starlight echoes back "To business" but it's hard to tell if she's serious or not.

"So, let's get to it — what do you think of when you hear the word 'business'?"

We mumble our answers, "Getting screwed," "Cheating," "Bad people," "Producers who rip you off."

"All this bad stuff...and yet," the Director says, "you are working hard to become professional clowns. How do you plan to make a living?"

Roger says, "I've got an agent for my magic act. She does the business." The rest of us nod — having an agent sounds like a good way to go.

The Director smiles. "In other words, you'll let other people do your business for you."

I try to think of a clever retort but sip my tonic water instead. Virginie, in a black bustier and a poodle skirt, downs her tequila shot and bangs the glass on table, but she doesn't say anything either. The Director waits a few more seconds and then says, "Here's another question — what do Charlie Chaplin, Lucille Ball and Prince all have in common?"

"I see what you're getting at," Bari says, "they were all great artists *and* they were all good at business, right?"

"Exactly!" The Director stands up, tipping the neck of his bottle toward Bari. "Charlie Chaplin started United Artists; Lucille Ball became the first woman to run a major studio, Desilu Productions; and Prince owned NPG Records. Here's to art and business!" He raises his beer but only a quartet of techies sitting near the window join him.

The Director adds, "The hard truth is this — how you do business will determine how you make art. How you do business will determine the art you will make."

There is an awkward silence and the techies go back to their beers. Roger finally asks, "Anyone need another one?" and a few folks go up to the bar. Once we're all back at the big table, the Director continues, "You are training to be professional artists. This means, for most of you, a lifetime of freelance work. There's a joke about freelancing — you work three times for every dollar you make: First you have to *get* the job, then you *do* the job and then you try to get *paid* for the work you've done."

No one laughs.

"It may not be funny, but it is true. And the better you are at getting jobs and getting paid for the work you do, the more time you have to be an artist. It's as simple as that."

We argue, saying that we are artists because we hate business, that artists are not accountants, that we're no good at selling ourselves.

"Wait, wait. It's not so hard. Nearly everyone in the world does business in one way or another. Take Ron, the guy who owns this bar. He works at least an hour a day doing business — inventory, bills, payroll, taxes. And for that hour of work he gets to serve drinks to a bunch of clowns and techies." He looks over at the quartet but they are busy drinking. "Professional artists need to do the same: at least one hour of business every day. In return, we get to have careers performing around the world."

An hour a day doesn't sound so hard, but when I try to think about doing it, I realize I haven't a clue where I'd start.

"So let's say you're doing your hour a day and it's paying off. Now how do you decide where to work, which gigs you should take?"

Bari says, "That's easy — take the gig that pays the most."

"Money is important, that's true, especially when you don't have much." Bari murmurs, "Amen to that." "You might have to go for the gig that pays the most but that could cost you a lot in the long run." The Director stands up, "At this point in our field trip, I would like to introduce an expert on this subject, my mom."

I imagine an old woman in flap-shoes and a fright wig stepping out from behind the bar.

The Director sits back down and adds, "She's here in spirit if not in body. When I was starting out, I called my mom up all the time to complain about the business of show business. She'd say," the Director switches to a New York accent that sounds both sweet and steely, "You are so lucky. In your job, every few months you get to question the basic assumptions of your life. Most people don't even think about these things for years and then, when they do, they have to spend a fortune going to a psychiatrist. You are so lucky."

The Director is back to his normal voice. "You are all lucky, too. But it's hard. Let my mom help you out with her 'Five Question Formula for Success.' Bari, you already got the fifth question, 'Will I make a lot of money?'" Bari takes a bow. The Director continues, "The first question is 'Will I grow as an artist?' If the answer to that question is 'Yes' then the answer to No. 5 can be 'No, it doesn't make a ton of money.' Can be, but it doesn't have to be. On the other hand, if you are not growing as an artist, you better be making bank."

The Director walks over to a chalkboard near the bar that has the lunch special written on it. He points to the board and nods to the bartender, who hands him a rag and a piece of chalk. As the Director wipes the rag across the board, he says, "In between 'Growing as an Artist' and 'Making Money,' my mom's formula has three other questions." He scrawls on the chalkboard, saying the words slowly as he writes them:

1) ART
2) Will I meet people who will help me grow?
3) Will I help or harm the world around me?
4) Will I have fun, go on an adventure and grow as a human being?
5) $$$$

"And speaking of money, the next round's on me." We start calling out our drink orders and chatting. The Director talks a little more about business, then lets us relax and enjoy the bar. I'm regaling Anita with a story about street performing in Boston when I look up to see the Director balancing a chair upside down on his chin. He stands there, chair legs almost to the ceiling, until the whole bar is quiet. Then the chair comes down and he's sitting in it, all with one smooth move. Everyone cheers, which the Director acknowledges with a tilt of his head.

"Before you go off to your weekends, I want to thank you for something. When I took the job with Cirque du Soleil, I answered 'Yes' to the last four questions — meet people, not much harm, adventure and money. I wasn't sure I would grow as an artist so I said 'No' to the first question. That was fine. It was enough that I would be helping my family, growing the school's reputation and investing in my future career. I thought, 'I don't need to grow as an artist.' Luckily, I did." He checks his beer, sees that it's empty and puts down the bottle.

"I grew as an artist because of you, my students."

We must be giving him some strange looks because he nods his head and adds, "It's true. You showed me the way. When I was learning my role on *Corteo*, I kept thinking, 'What would I tell my students to do here? What principle would I use there?' I tried to be a student, too, and take my own teaching to heart. I tried to do on stage what I ask you to do in class.

"Keeping you all in my mind — your questions, your challenges, your tenacious drive to be great clowns — that's what helps me grow as an artist. I am so lucky. I have students to learn from."

Jake's Journal #11, May 23

Big Idea:
- *Clowning + Business = Career*

Why is it important to me?
- *I need to do at least an hour of business every day.*
- *"Mom's Formula" makes business seem almost human, not so intimidating and sleazy.*

An hour a day of business:
- *Make stuff to tell the world about me and Ronni — photos, resumes, website, Facebook, videos.*
- *Find the people to send that stuff to. Make a list of my "web of relationships"; grow that web.*
- *Make a list of gigs I want, with three sections:*
  - *My 'A' list — dream jobs that are way out of reach.*
  - *My 'B' list — jobs that are a bit out of reach.*
  - *My 'C' list — gigs I'm pretty sure we can get.*
- *Research the companies on these lists:*
  - *Where are they? Who runs the show?*
  - *How do they hire or audition? When? Who do we need to talk with?*
  - *How much do they pay? How well do they treat artists? How long is their season?*
  - *Does anyone in my web of contacts know them?*
- *Send the right materials to the right person at the right time with, if at all possible, an introduction from the right person. Pray to the clown gods.*

Ah-ha Moment:
- *"Will I grow as an Artist?" is the big question.*

CHAPTER TWENTY-ONE

DANCING WITH THE AUDIENCE
LOS ANGELES, CALIFORNIA

Cirque du Soleil

AS I'M SHOWING MY BACKSTAGE PASS to the guard on a gorgeous SoCal day, the strains of Mozart's bass aria "Un dente guasto e gelato" suddenly echo off the blue-and-yellow canvas of the entrance tent. Vittorio, all 6 feet 10 inches of him, is slowly getting out of a cab. Still singing, he limps up behind me and leans a huge elbow on my head. "Un dente guasto e gelato, devoured by worms, gives me such pain! Tanto dolor! Oh, oh pain..."

His voice is so deep he sounds like God.

"Oh, my leg. Some testa di merda in a van knocked me off my bicycle. Help me, my little Clown Morto!" Vittorio insists on riding his bike, even through L.A. traffic, and he clearly paid for it today. The security guards wave us by and I help Vittorio lumber over to the physical therapist's corner of the Artistic Tent. It's Tuesday, the beginning of our week, so the assistant physiotherapist, Keiko, is still getting the various braces and bandages onto their carefully labeled shelves. Keiko is from Osaka, Japan, and perfected her English in the football locker room of the Texas Tech Red Raiders.

"I'm busier than a cat covering shit on a rock pile. You can sit your fat ass on the bed and wait." Vittorio roars with laughter and rattles off the Russian curses he learned from Alexei last week. I leave them, my giant Argentinian friend howling in pain and laughter as Keiko deftly checks his knee, cursing a blue streak in her Japanese/Texas accent.

I'm almost done with my makeup, just getting the skin under my eyes tight so I can make the vertical black line that the makeup designer finds so appealing. Vittorio hobbles into the dressing room and thumps down in his chair. My line wiggles, I curse and Vittorio admonishes me, "Basta! You are lowering the standards of the men's dressing room with this foul language." I ignore him and try to make the line look good enough. "You should not be mad at me, my touchy little clown. You should pity me. I am out of the show for the rest of the week. Tanto dolor! Oh, oh pain…" And he is off, alternately singing Mozart and cursing in Russian.

Vittorio's injury, painful as it is to him, gives me a chance to improvise with audience volunteers, which I love to do. At this point in the tour, I need something to look forward to. One of the greatest risks for a performer in a long-running show is getting bored. This is why, before every performance, I ask myself, "How will this show be better than yesterday's show? How will I be an artist today and not a hack?" Sometimes this means changing a moment in the show that hasn't been working. Sometimes I remind myself that even though I've done this show over a hundred times, the audience is here for their first time. Sometimes, especially here in L.A., I think about the producer who might be sitting in the front row scouting for some fabulous show. I often have to break one of my own rules and then I can be pretty sure it is only a matter of time before I have to try something new again. This is part of the art of a long-running show.

Whatever technique I use before a show, being an artist and not a hack is for my own mental health. I've met too many bitter clowns — they are no fun to be with, they are not happy and Bitter Clown is a role I could all too easily play.

The stage manager's calls, "Tapis Rouge!" and we're heading for showtime.

Now the riggers are striking the net after the flying act, I've handed my robe to an usher and I'm walking into the audience. The Ringmaster is whistling Verdi on the other side and the spotlight hits me in the aisle. This is when Vittorio and I usually dance. Instead, I put my hand out to a woman in an aisle seat. She is older than me so she might know how to waltz. She does.

My volunteer dances better than me, gracefully spinning out and back into my arms. I spin her out again and this time she gives a curtsey and holds her hand for me to kiss. I kiss her hand and she sits down exactly as the Ringmaster hits the last note of the Verdi. Beautiful. Everyone on our side of the audience cheers for my dance partner, who beams and gives a wave.

I am always looking for the moment when a volunteer gets a glint in her eye and starts to play. In improvisation, we talk about "making an offer" — my hand reaching out to request a dance — and then "taking an offer" — the woman dancing with me — and then making another offer — my dance partner adding a curtsey before sitting in time with the music. One person makes an offer, the other person takes that offer and then makes an offer in return, repeat and enjoy. This deeply human interaction is the key to clowning with audience volunteers.

Now I need to find a different audience member. They don't have to dance or even stand up, they just need to ask the Ringmaster to whistle some Mozart. I find a stylish young man sitting two rows from the stage:

"What would you like to hear next? Bach, Beethoven, Mozart, Brahms, Mozart, Schubert, Mozart, Chopin, Shostakovich, Mozart?"

The young man figures out the game and, after waiting a dramatic moment, says, "How about Mozart?"

A nice laugh from the rest of the audience, leaving me to finish with, "What a great idea! Ringmaster, some Mozart please."

Giving an audience volunteer the space to play is gold, even if the game is as simple as asking for Mozart. Many volunteer acts are just coercion — "Do this!" — or worse, when the performer ignores the volunteer after inviting them on stage. A volunteer is as much a partner as any performer and should be treated with respect. Only then can something authentic happen between two people, letting us enjoy genuine moments of improvisation, real surprises, real play.

Ducking to board the small plane that will fly me home for 36 hours, I see that my seat is right behind a mom holding her 8-month-old. The baby gets cranky as soon as we take off and I think, "Time for some homework." I tell my students to practice their skills at playing with volunteers whenever they are around a baby. Now it's my turn.

Keeping a baby engaged, especially one who is already upset, means making offers, usually by imitating the baby, taking their offers and keeping the game moving. Babies get bored if you don't change the game but they will cry or disengage if you change the game too quickly. Playing with babies is clown boot camp.

This baby plays with me between the seat backs for about 15 minutes, not a record but still pretty good. The mom thanks me a few times and, blessedly, the baby sleeps the rest of the way to Oakland International. On the shuttle home, I fall asleep myself, exhausted from the ten-show-a-week schedule and heartsick from being away from my own babies for too long.

SPOTLIGHT:
A Web of Relationships

A clown should use her core skills — discipline, empathy, tough-
ness and deep humanity — in her business dealings. Business is
based on relationships, which is what clowns do best. The popular
culture stereotype of clowns, and all artists for that matter, as flaky,
self-absorbed and bad at business should be avoided like any other
toxin.

Here are some tools for creating and maintaining relationships:

- Invitations: Invite lots of people to your shows, even if
  they can't come. An invitation is a warm way to say, "I'm
  thinking of you", while also letting them know you might
  be available for future work.

- Thank yous: A thank you note extends a relationship
  and opens up the possibility of a next step. Send notes
  to folks who come to your shows, to teachers, casting directors, anyone you want in your web of relationships. In
  your note, include specific things that you are thanking
  them for.

- Answer people within 24 hours. This should be obvious
  but many performers lose good gigs, and can even have
  their careers stall, simply because they don't check their
  in-boxes regularly.

- Be as disciplined in business as you are in rehearsal or
  on stage. When your name comes up, everyone should
  say, "She's great to work with!" and not "He's really good
  on stage but a bit flaky."

- Don't step on people on your way up — you will meet them all again on your way down. Use the Golden Rule.

There are a lot of details on the business side of clowning — negotiating contracts, taxes, budgets, legal issues, copyrighting material, insurance. Everyone needs to take care of these and, luckily, there are experts to help. Every professional clown should have a long-term relationship with a good tax accountant and a good entertainment lawyer.

Speaking of lawyers, I'll end with a word about contracts; they are not, as some performers believe, tools of the devil. Contracts should be the written agreement between two parties who want to work together. They remind us of what we agreed on when time has passed and the relationship is rocky. Negotiating a contract should not be a battle but rather a dance aimed at finding ways to work together. If one party in the negotiation is much bigger and stronger, like, say, Cirque du Soleil, get a lawyer to do your dancing for you. But you still need to read and understand every word of every contract that you sign, even if, like my *Corteo* contract, it is bigger than the Sunday New York Times.

CHAPTER TWENTY-TWO

WONDERLAND

Clown Conservatory

A STREETCAR, A BART TRAIN, two buses and 137 minutes later, I finally get from my apartment in the Sunset to an obscure Oakland public library. It's Saturday, my day of rest, but I've schlepped all the way over here to support my school. The second-year students, who spend most of their time sequestered in a rehearsal room behind the acrobatic gym, are doing their first public performance of *Wonderland*. Although we don't know any of the nine cast members well, most of my classmates and I decided we needed to repay them for coming to all of our performances.

I'm late and in my rush to get seated before the show starts I walk right past the theater. Luckily, a reference librarian sees the panic on my face and escorts me into a large sunny room lined with book-shelves. There are about 40 chairs set in rows facing a small stage area that is defined only by a rug. A big trunk is set in the middle of the rug.

Ronni has saved a seat next to her and I slide in just in time to hear a chord strummed on a ukulele behind me. I swivel my head and the opening song begins, a setting of "The Jabberwocky" played and sung by the whole cast. They stroll through the audience to the stage playing a trombone, an accordion and various percussion instruments, dressed in simple costumes that only hint at the famous Tenniel illustrations.

By the time the actors are singing the chorus again, "Twas brillig and the slithy toves…", the trunk is open and they are pulling out a hat rack, a tea set, juggling clubs, more musical instruments and an over-sized book. An actor opens the book and reads, "Alice was beginning to get very tired of sitting by her sister and of having nothing to do…"

A few lines later, Alice is following the White Rabbit down the rabbit-hole — Alice is flipped and twisted from one actor to another, stage left to stage right — while the book gets passed and the narration continues. I am completely charmed.

Soon the White Knight is pratfalling off the trunk, which is now his horse, and then Tweedledee and Tweedledum get a couple of kids up out of the audience to help them dress for their battle over the broken rattle. As the rest of the cast sings, the Tweedles get their volunteers to fight for them with foam swords, much to the joy of the volunteers.

Part of me is swept away by the world of Wonderland come to life and part of me is seeing everything we've learned at The Clown Conservatory seamlessly woven together.

I want to be up there!

One of the volunteers races past me on her way back to her seat and a new narrator says, "Looking all around her, Alice saw a large mushroom." And there is a large mushroom onstage, made up of the other eight cast members. One of the actors pops up on top of the human sculpture as the rest of the actors speak in unison, "Her eyes immediately met those of a large caterpillar, that was sitting on the top." Different actors morph from mushroom to caterpillar and back. Alice struggles to answer the caterpillar's famous question, "Who are you?" The mushroom morphs into an eight-person caterpillar walking across the stage and then, seamlessly, they are butterflies, one upside down on the other's back with their legs straddled in the air as wings.

Plates fly in the Mad Tea Party, the Lobster Quadrille involves some slick hip-hop acrobatics and the Knave defends himself against the accusation that he stole the tarts by singing, tap dancing and juggling all at the same time.

Finally the cast is packing up the trunk as they slowly sing, "A boat beneath a sunny sky, lingering onward dreamily in an evening of July…." They take a bow and stroll back through the audience to a final reprise of "Jabberwocky."

Ronni and I sit and don't say anything for a few minutes. This is exactly what I want to do and the cast is just one year ahead of me at school! But they aren't making any money; in fact they are still paying tuition. I don't have the option of a second year at school, at least not next year. Can anyone make a living with a show like *Wonderland*?

"That was good, huh?" Ronni is still staring at the now empty stage.

"Yeah" is all I manage in response, "Too good."

Jake's Journal #12, May 31

The Big Idea:
- Someday I might be able to put all of this together — acrobatics, juggling, dance, mime, music, acting, improv and clowning, the inside and the outside clown.

Why does this matter to me?
- Wonderland was so cool to watch and I bet it was even cooler to do.

Exercises:
- Get ready for the first-year student tour; think of it as Wonderland-lite.
- Work on my acro moves, especially the partner stuff with Anita and Dan.
- "Clowning" is the right word for what the second-year students do in Wonderland but it is not your grandma's clowning. This kind of clown can do everything well AND make it funny and charming and exciting and even invite the audience to play along.

My Ah-ha Moment:
- When Alice grew taller by stepping into Humpty Dumpty's hands as he lay on his back and standing there as he slowly stood up and lifted her way above his head.

CHAPTER TWENTY-THREE

ONE MORE CUP OF COFFEE FOR THE ROAD

DENVER, COLORADO

Cirque du Soleil

THE THIN AIR OF DENVER made our first week here exhausting but we are happy to be out of L.A. The Rocky Mountains instead of the 405 Freeway, bike rides along Cherry Creek instead battling buses on city streets and, for me, the relief of knowing I'll be going home soon.

I'm saying good-bye to my flying bed and my custom-made harness, to "Marionette" and "Helium" and 10-show weeks and shuttle bus rides. I am going back to my family and to directing my school again next year. Performing is wonderful and this tour has been exciting and glamorous and tough. Teaching young clowns, training them to be professional artists, is the challenge I want now. I did what I set out to do — follow my own teaching onstage in front of thousands of people for more than 250 performances. I've held myself to the standards I hold my students to. I've grown as an artist and now it's time to go home.

This tour has taken a toll on my family — when I'm home, my kids cling to me and are suspicious every time I walk out of the house. My marriage has become a household operations partnership. We've planned a week-long vacation, just the four of us, starting the day after I leave *Corteo*, our first step toward being a family again.

My replacement, Artie, arrived the other day. He's a clown I knew decades ago. Having him on site has brought back all my young-performer competitiveness, even though now it's a little unsightly. Yesterday, as I was stretching for the show, Artie started showing off for some of the aerialists. When I looked up from my straddle, there he was in a straight, strong handstand, better than mine even though he's a few years older than me. My sweet young friends were eating it up, saying that he should be an acrobat, not a clown. I had to go lift weights to avoid completely losing my concentration for the show.

So today, between shows, I invite Artie over to do some doubles acrobatics. After a few tries, we are able to hold a decent hand-to-hand — Artie doing a handstand in my hands. Not bad for a combined 105 years of acrobatic muscle. We come down to applause from the aerialists and teasing from the acrobats. A few moments later, Hilary, the General Manager of *Corteo*, calls me over to where she is leaning on the trampoline. "You can't break anything for at least another week, until Artie learns the show." I agree to be careful and start to walk away. Hilary adds, "Thank you. We'll miss you. Break a leg tonight." I turn back to thank her but Alexei, our brilliant Uzbek troublemaker, has slipped in between us. Hilary smiles; Alexei starts into a tirade; I walk away.

Every day, usually when we're warming up for a show or resting between shows, Hilary hangs out in the Artistic Tent, leaning on the trampoline. She always looks like someone with nothing better to do than watch us stretch, gossip and lift weights. She just stands there with a smile on her face, calm and inviting. And most days, Alexei gets up in her face with a complaint. Alexei is a smart man and his complaints are usually rooted in reality, but he clearly delights in making a scene.

I always wonder why Hilary puts herself right in Alexei's sights. Doesn't she know he's always going have something to complain about? No one would blame her for just staying in her office. But there she is, listening to Alexei, and then, after a few minutes, gently moving on to talk with someone else.

Hilary is a good general manager. We call her The Mayor of *Corteo* and, like any mayor, she's responsible for her entire town. Hilary keeps our village of 140 people from 26 different countries humming along the highways of the United States in 65 semis and assorted cars and buses. Injuries, cultural tensions, languages, exhaustion, homesickness and substance abuse are just a few of the things that could bring us to a grinding halt. She has to keep everyone in the village getting along well enough to put on 385 shows a year for more than 800,000 Cirque du Soleil fans. $250,000 is at stake every show, a half million dollars for a two-show day. If I've got the math right, by the end of the year she will have sent the headquarters in Montreal around $100 million in gross receipts.

Hilary spends a lot of time on conference calls, in staff meetings, working on spreadsheets and talking with department heads. But she never seems to be in a hurry and she finds time to hang out by the trampoline every day. Why?

Because she gets to see first-hand how we're doing: who is off by themselves, who is hurt, who the new couples are. She gets to hear what's going on from Alexei as well as from less volatile performers. And by letting Alexei publicly complain, she takes away some of his ability to be subversive — everyone sees Hilary getting an earful from Alexei and most of us sympathize with her.

In a way, I'm the Mayor of The Clown Conservatory. But unlike Hilary, I'm always in a hurry. Students and staff members invariably get my attention by saying, "I know you're busy but…" For years, I thought this was the right way to lead — let folks see that I am working hard on their behalf and, as a side benefit, limit the amount of time I have to listen to people complain.

Watching Hilary I realize that I've had it all wrong, that complaints are gold for a mayor. Being available, open and seemingly free of time constraints saves a leader a lot of headaches and, in the long run, a lot of time. I hope I will be a better mayor of The Clown Conservatory next year.

Hilary leaves the Artistic Tent and I go to my dressing table to get in makeup for the show. Each moment is starting to take on "last time" status and I'm trying to capture each person in my memory. I'm nostalgic already, even though I'm still here. Pre-nostalgia, maybe.

A week later I'm riding a gondola high up in the San Jacinto mountains with my wife and boys. We've spent the last few days near here in Southern California, climbing up rickety ladders in slot canyons to catch a view of the Salton Sea, buying Medjools, Abbadas and Barhis from the Oasis Date Garden in Thermal, and eating at Soul of China near our La Quinta hotel next to a couple with their Chihuahua in his own high chair.

Here in the gondola, my younger son is busy tracking a hawk that swoops within 30 feet of the window while my older son takes pictures of trees clinging to the mountainside. My wife and I are leaning against the back rail, arms around each other, feeling the air cool as we get closer to the summit. We're back. I'm back. We're in rhythm again.

SPOTLIGHT:
Diane (Pino) Wasnak

Diane Wasnak trained with the great mime Tony Montanaro at Celebration Barn in South Paris, Maine. She came to San Francisco in the mid-1980s to join Joan Mankin in creating the two-woman clown team Pino and Queenie Moon. They anchored the Pickle Family Circus for years. When Lu Yi arrived at the Pickles soon after, Diane became his star acrobatic student. She quickly learned, and started performing: partner acrobatics, teeterboard, hoop diving and Chinese pole. Later, Lu Yi would teach her the solo act that became her signature, riding backwards on a bike while flipping bowls from one foot to her head.

When Joan Mankin left the Pickles in the early '90s to focus on her acting and directing, I was hired to partner with Diane. The difference in our sizes, over a foot in height and more pounds than I care to admit, was the basic relationship of Pino & Razz. With director Tandy Beal, we developed acts where Diane was a mosquito, a pillow and my tiny tuxedoed prom date (I wore a huge pink strapless number). She also played Puck in two critically acclaimed productions of *A Midsummer Night's Dream* — I was her foil as Bottom. Early in rehearsals for our second show together, "Tossing and Turning," Tandy asked Diane to improvise a fairy tale. The hilarious gibberish-and-mime version of Goldilocks that she created on the spot became, with only a little refinement, a huge hit with audiences all across the U.S. and in Japan.

Pino was in most of the acts in the Pickle shows, doing at least five clown entrées, most of the acrobatic numbers and playing her baritone sax and accordion. In the late '90s, Cirque du Soleil hired Diane to play the little baby in *Mystere*, a long-running Vegas show. At the end of her 18-month contract, she created an act with her dog, Bonzer, and became a freelance performer.

I learned a lot from working with Diane, sometimes the hard way. Early one morning in a school gym in Iowa, we were setting up for a duet show and complaining about our lack of sleep, the terrible stage, the coffee. I remember thinking, "These kids don't care. I'll just give 50 percent and save my energy for the big show tonight." We got on stage and Diane, as always, gave 100 percent. The kids loved her and barely noticed me. After the show, I found myself packing the car alone as the kids swarmed around Diane, getting her autograph and telling her how great she was. I vowed to never "save my energy" again.

CHAPTER TWENTY-FOUR

SHAVING CREAM AND EGGS
Clown Conservatory

THE STICK COMES OUT OF NOWHERE, smacking against my cheekbone before rattling onto the floor of the old theater. It hurts like hell.

This warm-up, simply called "Sticks," is not for the faint of heart. The Director says the *Corteo* cast plays it before every performance so, on the first day of rehearsal for our final tour, we are playing too. The rules are simple: 1) throw your stick to anyone at any time and 2) catch the stick.

My classmates wait while I pick up my stick and get back in the circle. We all breathe together and touch the ground. I tell myself to keep my focus open, to see all the sticks all the time in order to avoid another smack in the face. This round, the action seems to slow down and, for a few moments, I can see everything.

"Good! Let's take one final breath together and ground ourselves." We follow the Director's instruction, touching the ground with one hand before putting the sticks away. "That makes me happy. I thought I was roadsick, which is the opposite of homesick, but now I realize I've just been missing Sticks. Even after playing it a few hundred times, I still love this game."

I think, "Then you must not have caught too many sticks on your cheek," but I don't say it.

"Starting right now, you are no longer students. You are a circus troupe. In 28 days, you start a tour, playing to hundreds of people in the course of your travels. You are getting a taste of professional circus."

I smile even though I know that our tour is only three weeks long, we won't leave the Bay Area and most of the folks we'll perform for are in schools, senior centers or hospitals. Still, it's a circus tour and I'm proud.

Ronni and I decide to do a classic American gag, the Chef Routine. We hope that scouts from Ringling or some other American circus will see our final show, or watch the video that the Director sends around, and book us. And we figure that kids will love it. But we're afraid that some of our teachers, especially the French Master, will find it too American, too slapstick, too "external." We don't tell anyone except Bari what act we're doing and we rehearse in the kitchen at Ronni and Bari's apartment at night instead of at school.

We spend as much time cleaning as we do rehearsing since the Chef Routine involves some eggs and a lot of shaving cream. (Professional clown tip: Never use real whipped cream since it gets into the costumes and starts to smell really bad.) Most of the act is a "Tit for Tat" where Ronni, the White Clown, and I trade blows — I break an egg in her hand, she breaks an egg on my head, and so on. It's already messy before we get to the big finale when I fill Ronni's chef's toque with shaving cream and put it back on her head. Now comes the hard part — I push down on the crown so a cream geyser shoots up through the hole on the top. It is surprising, funny and even beautiful to watch. It's also hard to get the right amount of cream with the right pressure. Ronni and I go through a lot of shaving cream and a lot of paper toques.

We decide to unveil our gag at the dress rehearsal. That will give us exactly one week before our first show at the Tenderloin Community School, plenty of time for our teachers to give us notes but not enough time for them to make us change the routine completely.

At the dress rehearsal, the trouble starts with the first words out of the Director's mouth, "Before we warm up with a game of Sticks, I want to let you know that from now on we will only have live music in the show. If you've been working with canned music, today is a great time to get some of your more musical classmates to help you out."

Damn! We choreographed our whole routine to a Scott Joplin rag, which Ronni has on a CD, ready to go for the dress rehearsal.

"I'm happy to play for any of you." It's Bari, opening up her accordion case.

"Wait a minute," I say, turning to the Director, "why can't we use the music we practiced with?"

"All the performers in a clown act, including the musicians, should be alive and in the same place when the act is performed. Musicians on a CD can't follow your improvisation or wait for an audience reaction or recognize a golden mistake. You have to play *to* a CD; you can't play *with* a CD. Unless you have live musicians, you can't genuinely play with the audience and play with the music at the same time. Everyone in a clown acts needs to breathe together, which means everyone needs to be present and alive."

Clearly I'm not going to win this argument so, right after Sticks, we play the Joplin tune for Bari. She learns fast and her accordion gives it a French accent. Dan and Starlight grab shakers, wood blocks and a duck call to do the sound effects. We only have a few minutes to prep our band but the dress rehearsal goes pretty well. Bari has seen us rehearsing in her kitchen and her music seems to bring out the best in my clowning.

Amazingly, the French Master loves our entrée and offers us lots of tips on the timing, how to set the props and, most importantly, he tells us to lay down a tarp before the show to make our clean-up easier. The Director gives us the honor of closing the show but then adds, "You have to go last because no one wants to perform on a stage full of broken eggs and shaving cream." I take this as a challenge — we will become the best act in the show and earn our position as closers.

The next six days are about repetition and adjustments. We do the act over and over again, grabbing anyone we can get to watch us. We learn something from each audience: The kids from the French school are wild and we match their energy, while an audience of beautiful aerialists brings out the bon vivant in both of us. We even take our tarp, eggs and shaving cream to Hippie Hill in Golden Gate Park and wait after each joke for the potheads to finally laugh. Often enough, we're still working when Bari gets home from her bartending shift so we get to run through the whole routine with music. Sometimes the neighbors complain about hearing clown accordion after midnight, so we have to stop.

We're rapidly chalking up the rehearsal hours — not yet 100 per minute of stage time but that formula doesn't seem like hyperbole any more.

Jake's Journal #13, June 14

The Big Idea:
- See everything all at once — you never know where that stick is coming from.

Why is it important to me?
- The Chef Routine is actually funny!
- We could get paid work if the right people see us having a good show.

Exercise:
- "Sticks"
- Rehearse the important details, like the cream geyser blow-off, until the execution is exquisite.
- Do our act over and over, for lots of different people, adjusting to every audience and making improvements after every show.
- Live music, not canned.

My Ah-ha Moment:
- When the sticks and the people and our throws and our catches were suddenly all in sync and we couldn't make a mistake and I stopped thinking about my aching cheek. How does that happen?

CHAPTER TWENTY-FIVE

ON THE ROAD
Clown Conservatory

OUR FINAL TOUR IS SUPPOSED to harden us up, turn us into pros, give us some real circus cred. With a week of touring still to go, we're already a slick, smooth traveling machine, a mini circus. Without a ring crew, we've been using our three layers of checklists — for props, for packing the van and for our backstage setup — to make sure we bring everything we need to every show and then home again. Without a front office, we've been making arrangements with principals and getting checks from nursing home directors, finding parking, schlepping prop boxes and sewing costumes. I know a whole lot more about the reality of professional circus than I did two weeks ago.

And our final tour continues to surprise me. I was sure that Virginie and Bari's reworked version of their outrageous "You Can't Smoke That Here" would never fly for the elementary school crowd. Amazingly, it is even better than before. Bari, as the Auguste, enters playing a tiny toy piano with all the spacey euphoria she had when she entered smoking a bong. The kids get unearthly quiet to hear the tinkling melody she plays and then howl when her entire body blisses out. Virginie's White Clown is every bit as edgy and mean as the Nazi nursemaid in her story but now, partnered with Bari's bliss-bunny Auguste, the kids love her, too.

On the other hand, our Chef Routine bombed that first performance at the Tenderloin Community School. The act before ours was a big hit, a dance routine featuring Dan, Anita and Dan's unicycle, all three of them in tutus. The 300 kids sitting on the floor of the multipurpose room ooh-ed and aah-ed at the grace and skill and then went wild when Anita chased Dan and his unicycle around and through them.

Because our act makes such a mess, we decided to set up far away from the audience. When we came on, juggling a few eggs and throwing some shaving cream pies ten yards from the front row, it wasn't such a thrill. To make things worse, the ceiling lights where we set up pointed straight down, leaving our faces in the shadows of our toques.

As the kids headed back to their classrooms, high-fiving the other clowns, Ronni and I cleaned up our mess. Back at The Clown Conservatory, we cornered the Director to get his advice for the next day's performance. "Take center stage, make sure you are well lit and find a better entrance."

The next day, we made our entrance by joining Dan and Anita's chase, establishing our relationship literally on the run, while Starlight and Roger set our tarp and table in good lighting center stage. By the third show, Ronni and I had earned our spot as the closing act.

Another surprise came at a school for deaf children. While we were loading in, 45 minutes before show time, a dozen shy first graders came in with their teacher and sat quietly in the back of the small theater. As Bari and I were putting down a prop box, we noticed Roger sitting with the kids, smiling in a way I'd never seen before. The next time I looked up from my load-in duties, the kids were all over Roger and my grandiose, talkative classmate was in heaven. No jokes, no magic, no words — just a lot of love.

When the show started, with Starlight announcing a magic act, Roger came onstage with a new confidence and grace. For the first time, he looked comfortable in his skin — and the kids loved him. A few minutes later, at the end of their act, Starlight amazed all of us by taking the linking rings out of Roger's hands and doing the final trick. She told us later they had been secretly working on that ending for weeks but it wasn't ready for prime time until now. Roger missed load-out and only got to the van on time because Anita practically dragged him away from the kids.

Our seventh show of the tour was in a big old theater in a center for severely disabled adults. The vans full of our audience members were already there when we arrived. We carefully steered our boxes and bags around wheelchairs and walkers. After we got all our stuff onto the raised stage and started to set up, we realized that our stage manager, Anita, wasn't there. Anita had taken to the job of running the show-behind-the-show with relish. Before each performance, she would march around backstage with her checklists on a neon pink clipboard and snap orders to us peons. When we did something wrong, she'd curse in Spanish under her breath. We complained a lot but relied on her to keep us organized.

Anita was in the hallway dancing with an old woman in a wheel-chair. A disheveled-looking man in his 20s was singing "Sweet Caroline" at the top of his lungs with an aide holding onto a strap around the man's waist to keep him from falling on the dancers. Like Roger at the school for the deaf, our perfect dancer had found her people. As the rest of us watched from the lip of the stage, Anita shimmied and shook as the man sang and the woman waved her arms. Pretty soon, the hall was filled with people, staff members and patients, all moving and singing and howling and laughing. It looked like a Brueghel painting come to life.

Later, when Anita chased Dan off the stage, the audience burst into "Sweet Caroline" and she danced with at least a dozen people while Dan idled on his unicycle. Our load-out was a disorganized mess because our stage manager was busy being mobbed by her fans.

The French Master has seen a couple of shows and helped us tighten up the Chef Routine. "Simplicity and logic" is his mantra. Now that we have the scheme of the gag in our bones, we've added couple of new juggling moves that are getting oohs and aahs. Ronni and I are serious about going on the road together after graduation so we're putting our marketing materials together whenever we aren't performing. One hour a day of business.

Even with the school tour going well, I'm tense. Ronni and I are the only members of our class who don't have a job lined up after we graduate. Roger was the first to get cast, auditioning by video for a small, hip Swiss circus and signing a contract before we even started our tour. A week later Virginie got an offer back home in France to work with a "cirque burlesque." It sounds right up her alley — lots of leather and a punk circus band. Then Bari found a job as musician/clown with a small San Francisco circus that tours the parks every summer; Anita got into the MFA program at Dell'Arte International, a theater school 300 miles north in Blue Lake. Starlight, who has been practicing her Spanish with Anita all year, is going to travel to Mexico City to try to join a circus that has its home base near Anita's old neighborhood.

As we were unpacking our props yesterday, Dan announced that he turned down a gig with Culpepper & Merriweather, a small American tent circus. He said he is going back to school for a masters degree in education. I was floored — how could he turn down a circus tour to go back to school, exactly the opposite of what I want to do? Dan said he would always perform but working with kids is what makes his heart sing. He even asked me to help him design a physics curriculum that uses circus skills to demonstrate the concepts. Of course I said, "Yes." When I dropped some heavy hints about wanting the Culpepper gig, he said they were only looking for a solo clown. Ronni and I have a deal, so I let it go.

Our final performance is tomorrow, back in our own theater. My parents flew in from New Jersey this afternoon and now they are treating me to dinner at Ebisu, a high-end sushi joint near the school. After drinking our miso soup and catching up on weddings, births and medical issues, the conversation lags. I'm nervous about them watching me throw cream pies at Ronni tomorrow night. The question of a contract with a professional circus doesn't come up. After dinner they plead jet lag, drop me off at my place and drive back to their hotel. I go over to Ronni's and we rehearse our act with Bari for an hour and then call it a night.

Today my parents insist on taking me to lunch and then driving me to the school, even though it will get them there three hours before showtime. My mother says, "We want to see your school, meet your teachers and the other students. And when you need to get ready for the show, we'll go explore the Haight Ashbury."

From the moment we walk through the front door, my dad is fascinated with everything, from the rigging to the German Wheel to the aerialists' biceps. I'm embarrassed but everyone else seems to like the attention. A gorgeous acrobat who I've never talked to whispers in my ear, "Your dad is so cute." My mother takes in the school with a more critical eye and, showing her around, I am excruciatingly aware of how old the building is, and how shabby.

The French Master is coming through the front door as my parents are heading out to explore the neighborhood. I make introductions and the French Master says, "Your son Jake, he is now a clown, non? Not, how do you say, prestigious like a physicist but..." He makes that French puffing noise with his lips and I want to strangle him on the spot. Instead, I go into the theater and do dive rolls until my arms ache.

Anita has us setting up chairs, hanging costumes and laying out our props. Since we're in our home theater, we've decided to remount the ensemble dance number from our second show and add a clown band piece that we've been working on with the Musical Director. As soon as the last prop is in place, Anita gets eight of us dancing while Bari accompanies on accordion. We look a whole lot better now than we did back in the fall.

After 30 minutes, even Anita is satisfied with the dance, "Good, good. Bari, don't let the tempo get slow, and dancers, listen to the music, please. Claro?" We all make agreeable noises as we try to catch our breath. "Bueno. Now let's sing our song a couple of times and then get in costume for meet and greet."

When rehearsal is over, I go into the old storage closet that we use as a backstage to spirit-gum a skinny white beard to my chin, slap a red-and-white striped hat on my head and strap on my three-foot stilts. It's Fourth of July weekend and I'm doing the pre-show as Dan Rice, the clown who is said to have been the model for Uncle Sam. Bari helps me walk down the steps, all 10 feet of me from stilt bottom to top hat. Dan sits on his unicycle and bounces down the stairs beside us. After the first flight, I'm steady enough so that Bari can let go and play her accordion. We stride, bounce and play our way down to the sidewalk.

At 10 minutes to show time, Anita calls us backstage to change for the show. The seats are already full of friends, family and, I hope, a few circus scouts. All of our teachers are sitting in the back, including the Director, who looks nervous.

He doesn't need to be — from the moment we start our opening number, the dance routine, the crowd is hooting and hollering. The Chef Routine kills and, after the clown band "Carmina Burana" number the audience gives us a standing ovation.

I walk into the house still wearing my sweaty, shaving cream and egg-splattered costume. My parents hug me hard, ignoring the mess. My mom even hugs Ronni, who stiffens but then hugs back. Before anyone has a chance to say anything, the Director interrupts us. He drags over a tired-looking man in slacks and a herringbone sports coat who he introduces as the Ringling Bros. and Barnum & Bailey Circus Performance Director. The Performance Director completely ignores my parents, shakes my hand and then Ronni's and says, "Do you two want to replace a couple of clowns who just left the Blue Unit? You'll have to start right away."

Ronni and I immediately say, "Yes!" completely forgetting the Director's rule about never agreeing to a job until you've carefully studied the contract.

"Good. You'll be performing for 20,000 people a show so we're going to need to work on your makeup and costumes. You can do that chef gag in the pre-show and learn the production numbers on the road. Call me tomorrow." He hands us each his card, turns and leads the Director off to meet some of our classmates. Ronni and I stare at their backs. My dad winks at me, my mother sighs and then gives me another hug, whispering, "You earned this."

CIRCUS TRAIN

I SEE THE SUN RISING OUT OF THE BIG, grimy window of my tiny room on the Ringling Bros. and Barnum & Bailey circus train.

My room. On a circus train.

I'm thinking about how fast my schooling ended and my professional circus life began. Everything I'll need for this year with the Ringling Blue Unit is shoved into an old-fashioned steamer trunk. Sitting on my bunk, I see the sorghum fields of the Great Plains fly by as the train heads to its next stop — Las Vegas.

Ronni and I flew into Lincoln, Nebraska, yesterday. We went straight from the airport to our seats on the lower level of a huge arena. We madly took notes on everything in the show, especially the clown numbers. After the finale, we stayed in our seats until the audience had cleared out, watching the ring crew strike some aerial equipment.

The boss clown, a tall, thin man in whiteface with a tuft of red hair attached to the top of his bald pate, waved for us to come down into the ring. He gave the high sign to a couple of security guards and led us backstage, past the floats from the finale and the motorcycles from the Wheel of Death, to Clown Alley. We walked into a large dressing room in the bowels of the arena filled with steamer trunks and bright costumes. Tubs of makeup, brushes and powder socks sat on the counter in front of the mirrors that lined three walls. We met the ten clowns who will be our partners for the next year. They all managed to wave while taking off their makeup in various stages of undress.

After everyone was cleaned up and back in civvies, we helped them hang costumes and caught a ride back to the train with another Clown Conservatory alum. The boss clown arrived a few minutes later and showed us our rooms, which are next door to each other in a car with some other clowns and a few band members. As he was heading back to his room a few cars over, he said, "It's a long jump to Vegas but we'll have a few days to rehearse at the arena when we get there. The train leaves in a couple of hours. Get some sleep."

Ronni and I sat in her room drinking celebratory beers and talking about our new life. We laughed a lot, made some promises to each other and tried to walk through one of the clown production numbers without much success. We joked about some of the lamer acts in the show and argued about which showgirl was the hottest. We ended up agreeing that the woman who got shot out of the cannon took the cake.

Now it's 7 am and I've been up since 5 staring out the window. The rhythmic clatter of the wheels on the tracks, the sunrise, the flat fields of America. I stand up to stretch and my fingers touch both walls. It's cozy in here. I'm home.

THE END

CIRQUE DU SOLEIL

AUDIENCES EXPERIENCED a *Corteo* performance as two hours and 40 minutes of light, music and movement; the cast and crew experienced each show as part of a long string of shows in a long list of cities. For me, there was a rhythm to the show and rhythms of the road that combined to create the structure of my life.

The show rhythm started with arriving at the tent, flashing my badge at the security guard and signing in, then makeup and warm-up, my cue to lie on the bed in the middle of the stage and the organ riff that started the first act; the ebb and flow of scenes and costume changes and then intermission. The second act, flying across the stage on the bike for the final scene, the bow and taking off makeup four hours after putting it on. Unless it was a two-show day, in which case I'd leave the makeup on, eat, nap and get ready to start over again.

The rhythm of the road went week by week — Monday to rest, no show; Tuesday, Wednesday and Thursday to iChat with my family, do chores and work in my mobile office until it was time to ride my bike or catch the shuttle to the tent. Friday, Saturday and Sunday were two-show days, mainly rest until it was time to get in makeup. I spent about 50 hours a week at the tent plus 20 hours of work from my mobile office and still had more free time than when I was home running the school and raising two boys.

There was a bigger road rhythm as we went city to city — the easy first few days in a new town with only a couple of rehearsals and time to get used to a new site, a new apartment and a new neighborhood.

Then the dress rehearsal audience, which was small and rowdy, followed by the larger, sometimes staid opening-night crowd, who rowdied up at the after-party in the VIP tent. Then a month or two of shows before we got to the closing week, when the backstage population of 140 swelled to more than 200 with local hires and "fly-ins," the tough-looking teardown specialists from Montreal. On Wednesday, dozens of forklifts appeared on site and crept closer to the tent every day. As the closing week progressed, things started to disappear — an awning went, then the weight-lifting set, the trampoline, chairs, mats, half of the cafeteria. The final show in a city felt like a race — would we finish the performance before they took the tent down?

These rhythms always had the potential to become a grind. Parties, river rafting, evenings off at the theater and, of course, the week at home between cities, were highlights that kept boredom at bay. Technical glitches, like the soundboard crashing or a computer malfunction, gave us a shot of adrenaline from time to time.

There were also built-in highlights such as Sticks, which would, on some days, be a painful mess and on others would be a ballet with every hand in the right place for every catch. Sticks, where anyone can throw at any time to anyone else and everyone has to be prepared to catch at any time, was a perfect metaphor for performing in a big, high-tech circus with the audience sitting on both sides of the stage.

Some of my 13 scenes, and the little rituals between scenes, would give me juice — chasing a pair of clown shoes across the stage, playing the tuba and coaxing ethereal sounds out of the glass harmonica, watching six acrobats in pajamas romp on trampolines dressed as Victorian-era beds, floating into the darkness of backstage on a bike suspended 20 feet into the air as the audience gave us our final ovation.

Coming offstage after our last show in a city was my favorite time. We would all quickly get out of costume and clean off our makeup so we could pack up everything left inside the Artistic Tent. The dressing consoles, costumes, drapes, poles, juggling clubs and trapezes — everything had to be loaded into boxes and onto the semi trucks in less than an hour. Sixty performers working hard and fast, sweating and grunting and cursing in 20 languages. It was Sticks done with huge rolling road cases. And then we were done.

The tech crew and fly-ins would work all night and for ten more days until *Corteo* was loaded onto 65 trucks and then set up in the next city. I would say good-bye in as many languages as I could manage and head back to the apartment to pack for my week at home.

I did 385 performances in seven U.S. cities and another 115 shows in Nagoya, Osaka and Tokyo. *Corteo* closed in 2015 after a 10-year world tour. The last time I saw the show, during its Paris run in 2011, it looked fresh and vibrant. Pierre-Philippe Guay, who was then play-ing the Dead Clown, made the role I had done 500 times seem new and fascinating. As of this writing, I am still working for the casting department after years of doing workshops for the performers in many Cirque du Soleil shows. My old *Corteo* friends have had babies, joined other shows, started their own companies and made films and CDs.

As my wife predicted, working for Cirque du Soleil has done things for me and my family that we couldn't have imagined when I was first offered the role of the Dead Clown. In many circles, having "starred in Cirque du Soleil" on a résumé is shorthand for "he's for real." Since Cirque is a global brand, I have a calling card anywhere in the world. Staying connected with the company and many of the artists who work for Cirque leads to new adventures.

Some of my former students have performed with Cirque du Soleil. Two of them, Joel Baker and Jonas Woolverton, were working in dif-ferent shows in Las Vegas and offered my wife and me a 24-hour Vegas vacation complete with a hotel room and tickets to both of their shows in one night. Before the early show, LOVE, Joel gave us a backstage tour and then, having an hour before the house opened, invited us to the clowns' dressing room. As he got in makeup, Joel and I happily talked shop while my wife was entertained by a half dozen half-naked clowns from five different countries.

Eighteen months after leaving the U.S. tour, I had the pleasure of rejoining *Corteo* for a short stint in Japan, doing the role of the Dead Clown in Japanese. I learned the eight pages of dialogue from a tutor who told me, when I thought I had it nailed, that no student of hers was going to sound like a tourist on stage. We worked together for another month.

Alison Crawford, the Senior Artistic Director who had originally cast me in *Corteo*, came to see the show in Osaka and told me after-ward that I looked more relaxed, more natural, than I had in the U.S.

I realized that performing for an audience with whom I didn't share a language in a country where no one knew me took away a layer of tension I wasn't even aware was there. In Japan, I could walk on stage and, metaphorically, say, "Hello, my name is Jeff" with a little less of a mask.

My family joined me in Japan for a month, a magical time of delicious food and ancient temples, high-tech toilets and bullet trains, the Peace Museum in Hiroshima and the aquarium in Osaka. At the corner grocery store in Nagoya, my older son mimed an onion for a clerk — slicing and crying — who excitedly led him to the produce section; in a tiny restaurant in Osaka, my younger son sat at the bar and ate every strange food the owner offered him. At the end of the night, after the owner had entertained us with Korean karaoke and we were on the street looking for a cab home, she ran out with two big boxes of dried seaweed for my son. He was very proud.

My boys are great travelers and lovers of new tastes, new sights and new people. Touring with the show, which often felt like a burden on the family, also gave them gifts. Unlike the Gentiles, who are living a modern version of the classic traveling circus family life, my family doesn't perform. Our home is separate from the tent and, at the same time, we are a circus family.

THE CLOWN CONSERVATORY

PHILOSOPHY

"Growth as an actor and growth as a human being are synonymous."

– Stella Adler Studio

"A few modern philosophers...assert that an individual's intelligence is a fixed quantity, a quantity which cannot be increased. We must protest against this brutal pessimism... With practice, training, and above all, method, we manage to...literally become more intelligent than we were before."

– Alfred Binet, the inventor of the IQ test (as quoted by Carol Dweck)

PEGGY FORD AND I SHARED these beliefs with the Adler Studio and M. Binet. We realized that we were in the business of training whole human beings, not just performance virtuosi. Our criteria for entrance into the school went beyond "most talented" — we didn't even use the word talent, a stance that is now supported by Dweck's research on fixed vs. growth mindsets.

The Clown Conservatory trained adults to work as professional circus clowns. Many of our graduates are performing in circuses around the world. Some of the 130 students who graduated during my tenure as director have used their training in other professions, from the allied arts such as theater, music, film and puppetry to teaching, producing, burlesque dancing, farming, running youth programs and working with incarcerated women. One uses his clown skills to navigate between computer geeks and FBI spooks in his job as a big data analyst.

Without having the words, Peggy Ford and I approached auditions with a "growth mindset." We were looking for interesting people who could grow as artists and human beings, people we wanted in our school for a couple of years and in our lives for decades. Then we designed a program to support dynamic, engaged lives in the circus ring, on stage or anywhere else.

One spring, a young woman auditioned for us with a particularly awful act and then followed up with an even worse interview. We were in the middle of a long day of back-to-back auditions so, when the candidate walked out of the room, I just turned to Peggy and said, "That's an easy decision." Peggy cheerfully agreed, "Yep, it is. She's in."

"Did you see what I saw? That audition was terrible."

"Yep."

"And she bullshitted her way through the entire interview."

"Yep."

"Oh, you're joking." And I put the candidate's picture and résumé in the reject pile.

Peggy snatched them up. "She's in. She's funny looking. She'll learn the rest."

By the end of the school year, this young woman had a contract with a big circus and she now runs her own theater company. She grew into funny, real funny. She wasn't a born clown, she wasn't "talented," but she could grow and Peggy saw that.

Peggy and I sometimes caught flack from visitors who looked at our motley crew and asked, "Do really believe that any of these students will become a world-class clown? Really?" I would always try to defend my fledgling clowns but I now know that this was not the right question. "World-class clowns" wasn't our only goal. We were training human beings in the art of clowning and, luckily, there are many different paths open to a professional clown.

It is common to hear circus people say clowning cannot be taught. "A clown is born a clown." This is no more true for clowns than it is for musicians or painters; that is, it is true to a certain extent. Some people have a great aptitude for music or visual arts or clowning. They have a musical or spatial or kinetic "intelligence," as Howard Gardner would put it. But there are basic tools of the craft that everyone, even the most gifted, needs to learn in order to become a true artist. I have found that tenacious outstrips gifted almost every time. Great tenacity plus great gifts makes for superstars like Bill Irwin. Great gifts without tenacity is often heartbreaking.

Early on we had a star student, a world-class clown-in-the-making. He could do it all — acrobatics, music, pratfalls, dance — with the light grace of Danny Kaye. By the end of the school year, though, all the other students had passed him by. They had grown and he stayed fixed. If there is such a thing as "talent," we saw that it was overshadowed quickly by curiosity and risk-taking.

We were also aware that if we had a ballet school, or even the aerial program that Elena Panova ran in the gym next door, the jobs our students would be auditioning for would be more proscribed. We might have had to audition potential students with different criteria in mind. Luckily, clowning *is* a growth mindset — clowns are voracious and omnivorous and adaptable, like weeds.

In shaping the curriculum of The Clown Conservatory, the question I asked was, "How did I actually learn?" The answers to this question are very different than the answers to "How did my teachers teach?" I learned performing on the streets, in workshops, from other performers, from a few good mentors and from Dell'Arte School of Physical Theater (now Dell'Arte International). And I learned from audiences — circus audiences, theater audiences, kindergarteners and corporate party-goers.

I was a terrible student and that shaped my career. I had to be tenacious, using the one skill I had, juggling, to get into school (I taught circus classes in exchange for tuition). Juggling got me in front of audiences and into shows with people who were much better than me. Being a bad student also helped me learn to be a good teacher — I can understand and empathize with the slowest learner in any class.

Our curriculum was designed to give the students a faster path than I had meandering through a freelance career. I wanted them to become better than me faster. Of course, I used the ideas of my teachers at Dell'Arte International, my mentors like Jael Weisman and the giants in the field such as Jacques Lecoq. But I always asked the question, "How did this idea or exercise work for me? How else did I learn?"

We built a pedagogy that is different from other clown programs. We also designed in challenges to our pedagogy so it didn't become a system or a codified technique.

We made it a point to bring in guest teachers, like John Gilkey and Ronlin Foreman, who approach clowning very differently than the way we were teaching. We trusted that students would take it all in and eventually find their own unique path.

I often said that The Clown Conservatory was part trade school and part art school; we taught the crafts needed for a career in the circus and theater industries and we trained artists to grapple with difficult issues and work in diverse communities. We found that these goals are complementary and necessary to have in tandem. An artist has to offer an audience art, a specific and interesting way of looking at the world. Artists also need craft, which is all the tools we use to make our art engaging to the audience.

Many people who teach clowning start with character, which seems obvious since character is what we most remember about a clown — her makeup, costume, how she moves and makes us laugh or cry. Although we did address character at The Clown Conservatory, our main focus was on structure (routines) and skills (acrobatics, dance, mime, music, circus skills). These are crafts that are teachable. They gave the framework for students to develop characters.

Clown Conservatory students' characters emerged slowly over the course of their schooling and their careers. Rich characters take time and often evolve from performing good material with good people over and over. Many young clowns have trouble building a character while learning clown skills and creating good material. Giving students classic routines allowed them to concentrate on performing without having to also be a playwright. Within a classic gag, a student can experiment with different skills, walks, weight and other physical characteristics that are the building blocks of character.

For classic material, we taught everything from Commedia dell'arte lazzi to simple silent gags, classic European clown entrées to Beijing Opera scenes. In approaching these structures, Dominique Jando had the best advice: "Make the most vulnerable choice naturally." We asked the students to approach these routines as themselves, to be natural and to tell the story as simply as possible, bringing their own sense of humor to each strange new set of structural rules. Often students who had acting training struggled at this point, trying to find their way to a character. In clowning, the character begins with oneself, or possibly a slice of oneself. Usually that slice is one we want to hide from the world. Clowns live our most embarrassing selves out loud. But this cannot be self-indulgent — being oneself does not mean abandoning history and craft and all the tools that clowns have used for hundreds of years.

When it came time to explore the playwriting side of clowning, we started by offering a unit in storytelling. We arranged the audience in an old-time circle around a campfire, without the fire. If a clown can tell a simple story to a circle of folks, as humans have been doing for centuries, he has a good chance of being able to put together a clown routine that, as Geoff Hoyle says, is "logical and simple."

A clown has the most immediate, intimate and complex relationship with an audience of any performing artist. Much of the art we offer *is* the relationship with the audience. We don't just engage with the audience, we listen to them, we let them affect us and change us. We need them and they should know it. We play with the audience as we would play with another clown — we play for keeps.

Clowns need to be with audiences in order to grow. When students have good material to work with, they can focus on this relationship with the audience, as well as on their partnerships with their fellow clowns and with their props. When a clown is tuned into her audience good things happen — her character, timing and structure become richer and funnier.

HISTORY

In 1999, the Executive Director of Circus Center in San Francisco, Pat Osbon, asked me to write the artistic statement for a grant he was sending to the National Endowment for the Arts. It was a grant to start a clown school. I had become convinced that, in order to train the next generation of American clowns, there needed to be more than the short-term workshops that constituted most of the training in the U.S. I also was interested in the challenge of creating a full-year curriculum on clowning, so I agreed to write part of the grant although

I was skeptical that we would get funded and, even if we were, I was concerned that there would not be enough interest to sustain a comprehensive school (I had taught at Ringling Clown College in '96 and '97, its final two years).

We got $20,000 from the NEA in early 2000 and Pat asked me to start the school. He agreed that I would be the director, working with Peggy Ford, the former director of Make*A*Circus and an early graduate of Clown College, to create the structure of the program. We tested the market with a series of workshops that filled up quickly with good students from around the world. We then started The Clown Conservatory in January 2001 with 10 students taking 10 hours a week of classes — four hours of acrobatics with Weng Xiao Hong, two hours of Circus Skills with me and four hours of Core Clowning with Peggy, me and others.

The first graduates performed in the Circus Center student showcase in June 2001. We started our second year, a nine-month program, in September 2001 with 16 students. I left the school in 2010 and Peggy left soon afterward.

Peggy was the Dean of Students, setting up and overseeing a strong work-for-tuition program, helping students with housing, talking with them when their lives got hard and giving them hell when they didn't pay, came late to class or messed up in other ways. She also taught clown makeup and booked lots of student performances outside of school, including the annual Sisters of Perpetual Indulgence Easter Party for children in the Castro district. As we grew, my job as Artistic Director expanded beyond teaching and overseeing the curriculum to include directing six performances a year, booking guest instructors, and recruiting students from around the world. Caroline Jones, Sarah Hylas and then Jeni Johnson helped us manage the program; Paoli Lacy, Joan Mankin and Patty Gallagher were Associate Directors at different times.

Over the years, we added:
- A Body Awareness class, focused on Alexander Technique, taught at different times by Leslie Felbain, Jim Donak, Shelley Senter, Christina Vecciato (class of '01) and Adam Venker (class of '02)

- A dance class taught by Mina Liccione (class of '02) and then Joanna Haigood
- Letitia Bartlett's mime class
- A Guest Teacher program that included Ronlin Foreman, Mooky Cornish, Avner Eisenberg, John Gilkey, Joan Shirle, Joel Schechter, Keith Terry, Keiko Shimosato, Liebe Wetzel and many others.

Judy Finelli took over the Circus Skills class in 2006. Johannes Mager was our musical director, William Hall taught improv and Joan Mankin lead the physical theater classes. Additional staff members worked with me in the Core Clowning class: Dominique Jando taught clown entrées, John Warren worked with me to develop "Documentary Clowning," Jubilith Moore taught Asian theater, Patty Gallagher taught Balinese dance and Paoli Lacy introduced the students to clown therapy. Paoli also directed the school from 2010 to 2011.

In the third term, the students toured to local schools, senior centers and medical facilities, offering 10 to 14 performances to more than 1,000 Bay Area children and adults. The final show, performed in a theater, was videotaped and an edited DVD sent to casting agents around the world. Our Advanced Program created two shows, *Wonderland* and *Monkey King: A Circus Adventure*, that played extensively in theaters, schools and libraries in Northern California. Johannes Mager wrote the music for both plays and Doyle Ott was the dramaturg, helping me wrestle 100 chapters of the Chinese epic *A Journey to the West* into a script for *Monkey King*.

The Clown Conservatory partnered with New College to create EPI/CC, the only Master of Fine Arts program for clowns in the country. We also partnered with Coastal Carolina University to offer a Bachelor of Fine Arts in Physical Theatre that featured a senior year at The Clown Conservatory. Unfortunately both of these programs were short-lived — EPI/CC ended when New College closed its doors in 2008 and the BFA program, which was created by Paoli Lacy, was tabled when she retired in 2011.

Our Clowning in Community thread included projects such as clowning on Bay Area Rapid Transit, "Fools for War" in the anti-Iraq war demonstrations, the Lysistrata project at the Magic Theater, work with the Faithful Fools in the Tenderloin and our in-depth relationships with S.F. General Hospital and Rooftop Elementary School. At the hospital, students received training from nurses, psychologists and child life specialists in preparation for conducting interviews with patients, staff and family members and then distilling their experiences into material to be performed back at the hospital and elsewhere. We worked on the pediatrics ward and the long-term adult care unit; taught workshops in English and Spanish with C.A.R.E., a cancer support group; and even offered a clown class to hospice workers. At Rooftop school, the clown students received training in arts education and offered after-school workshops and Family Art nights.

TEACHING TECHNIQUE

The craft of teaching is as rich and complex as the craft of clowning. Over the years, I've been blessed with some great teaching mentors, including Kit Voorhees, Sabrina Klein and Tandy Beal. Here are some ideas and techniques I shared with The Clown Conservatory faculty about running their classes.

Multiple Modalities:

Howard Gardner's work on Multiple Intelligences is gold for any teacher. To simplify his complex ideas down to a shorthand, students learn in multiple ways. There is great power in inviting students to use multiple modalities when they are learning any subject. Modalities include:

- Kinetic (moving)
- Linguistic (talking or writing)
- Visual/Spatial
- Musical
- Mathematical
- Emotional
- Intellectual
- Spiritual

Scaffolding:

Scaffolding means having each exercise lead to the next, starting in a place that is accessible to everyone, and then, step by step, taking the students where they didn't think they could go or didn't know existed.

- Always plan more than you have time for so you can add or subtract layers of scaffolding. If the students get lost, add in more scaffolding; if they are picking up the concepts more quickly than you anticipated, skip a step or two.
- Practice your lessons on friends and colleagues to get the feel of the flow. Carefully word the prompts for each level of the scaffold so that your instructions are clear and simple. Losing momentum in transitions will kill the energy.

Shaping the Room:

In every class, I try to change the "shape of the room" (how the group is arranged) about every eight minutes. I got this formula from a third grade teacher and it seems to work for all ages. For example, I'll start with the group sitting in a circle for eight minutes, then working in pairs, then each pair performing for an audience followed by groups of eight and back to a circle. Of course, it doesn't always work out exactly this way but I keep this in mind when I write my lesson plans.

Witnessing Work:

When students create something in class, it needs to be witnessed by someone but not necessarily by the whole class. If time is running short, you can have each student or group of students show another student or group the piece they have been working on. This will take less time than having each group perform in front of the whole class.

Lens Questions:

When students are watching other students' work, I often give a lens for the group to look through. For example, "As you watch this next piece, notice how they use rhythm," or "As you watch this next group, notice how they use contrast." You can then do a quick "popcorn" after the performance to find out what they noticed. This does a few good things: it gives the audience an action and a focus, and it reminds everyone of the key elements of the work while helping students stay focused when watching the same exercise over and over again.

Reflection:

Reflection is a crucial part of learning. As a kinetic learner, I have been working hard to integrate reflection into my teaching work. Take pains to insure that reflection does *not* become direction or critique — those are different things.

I use the following formula as the structure for reflection:

- "What did you see? What did you hear?" followed by...
- "What did you feel? What did you think?"

This helps us all get beyond "I liked it" or "I hated it" or "You should have done this my way." It helps people look at artistic work as artists. Also, consider Multiple Modalities when you are designing reflection activities — can they draw their reflections or dance them or act them out?

William Hall has a great reflection technique — he often gives students a minute or two to talk to each other about the exercise before he debriefs in the big group. This requires participation from everyone and helps the students to:

- understand that they are responsible for discovering the value of the work they do.
- learn how to talk to each other about the work as opposed to filtering it through the instructor.

One of the unexpected benefits is that students will often think of something that the teacher didn't think of. The students can teach the teacher about the depth of an exercise.

Concepts:

- "Experience before explanation" is basic to the Lincoln Center Institute teaching methodology. When teaching something new, words often don't mean much and concepts have no context, until it has been experienced.
- "Observation, sensation and reflection" is another powerful teaching structure that is particularly useful when students are watching a video or seeing other artists work live.
  - Observe others doing the work (e.g., a Buster Keaton video).
  - Have the sensation of what it is like to do the work oneself (try one of Keaton's routines).
  - Reflect on what one has seen and felt with one or more people.

Improvisation:
Watch for the telltale signs of students tuning out. Be ready to change your lesson plan or insert an activity on the spur of the moment. Something in stark contrast to what you are working on can be powerful — for example, take three minutes to teach spit-takes in the middle of a serious class on negotiating contracts. Use your own improvisation and clowning skills as a teacher.

THE SECRET: A LITTLE LOVE ON THE SIDE

When our elegant and whip-smart office manager Caroline Jones had her first child, we dedicated a block of work-for-tuition hours to babysitting. A student would leave her morning classes sweaty and tired, babysit for 60 minutes and come back for the afternoon smiling and energized. Taking care of Caroline's baby was the best thing that could happen to a clown student. When the baby started eating solid food, Caroline, who made baby food from scratch, would pack extra for the babysitter. Taking care of the caretaker.

When students were having serious trouble in their lives or thinking of leaving school or were in danger of getting kicked out, Peggy Ford or Paoli Lacy would take them to lunch. They would talk. Peggy or Paoli would listen. Advice was given. If I was the problem, Peggy or Paoli would take me aside. Whether the student stayed or left, they knew they were being heard and taken care of. Most stayed.

Juan and Flory Cardenas kept the building clean and well loved. That was their job. They could also change your day in 30 seconds, with a hug or sometimes "You look tired, what's wrong?" or just a wave as you rushed out the door to your next class. They kept me and my hard-driven faculty and students soft.

Joan Mankin, our physical theater teacher, was diagnosed with fontal lobe dementia shortly after performing in the memorial show for Paoli Lacy. Students quickly found ways to be with Joan — onstage, walking her dog, swimming with her in the Bay. When we were planning a big benefit show for Joan at the Geary Theater, students rushed to volunteer to perform, to usher, to do whatever was needed.

Caroline, Peggy, Paoli, Juan and Joan all died between 2011 and 2015. The love they gave to students came back when they needed it most. Students performed in benefit shows and memorials, of course, raising money for medical care, legal fees and for a fund for young women clowns. Students also did the emotionally and physically hard work of caring for the dying. They visited in the hospital and made late-night runs to the pharmacy. They sat at Peggy's bedside when she became housebound, helping with the oxygen tank, cooking for her and playing music. Paoli directed Peggy's memorial show right before her cancer came back hard. When she started home hospice, students signed up for shifts giving her meds, emptying her bedpan and sleeping on the floor in case she needed help in the night.

Clown Conservatory students are people I want in my life. I love watching them perform in big shows like Ringling or Cirque du Soleil and, equally, in small cabarets, theaters, parks and bookstores. I love sitting in a café, sipping a cup of green tea latte and hearing about a former student's life. Growth as a clown and growth as a human being are synonymous, for all of us.

GRATITUDE

If it takes a village to raise a child, then it took most of a city to make this book. My first thanks are to the people closest to home: my wife, Sherry Sherman, and our boys Micah Sherman-Raz and Joshua Sherman-Raz. They inspire me every day. My mother, Mickey Spencer, who was a visual artist and a sociologist, and my brother, Jonathan Raz, who was a biostatistician and a poet, have also inspired me, along with the many other artists in our family.

Next, thanks go to our metaphorical neighbors, the folks who read various drafts, including Sherry, Janet Goulston, Joel Schechter, Phil Weglarz, Sara Moore and Patty Gallagher, followed by my editor, Douglas Cruickshank, and the other people who helped make a manuscript into a book — Erfert Fenton and Tracy Cox. Director Calvin Kai Ku and everyone who is part of the Medical Clown Project, an organization that Sherry and I created after I left The Clown Conservatory, has helped extend my understanding of clowning outside of the ring and into medical facilities and even private homes.

The rest of the neighborhood is filled with people who lived the story of this book with me — the students and faculty of The Clown Conservatory, the cast and crew of *Corteo*, the audiences and friends, acrobats, aerialists and fans, van drivers and bodega owners.

Looking out across the metaphorical city, I see many people who have dramatically shaped my career and my ideas about clowning and teaching — Jael Weisman; Lu Yi; Tandy Beal; Paoli Lacy; Peggy Ford; Diane Wasnak; Augusto Boal; Janet Goulston; Nina Wolf; Kit Voorhees; Sabrina Klein; Terry Sendgraff; Dan Mankin and Mark Sackett; Avner Eisenberg and Julie Goell; Alison Crawford, Richard Dagenais and Valentyna Pahlevanyan; Geoff Hoyle, Larry Pisoni and Bill Irwin; Joan Schirle and four decades of students and faculty at Dell'Arte International.

Finally, a huge "thank you" to all the students, teachers and performers who keep the ancient art of clowning alive, growing and relevant. If you dog-ear these pages, drip sweat on the cover and write notes in the margins, this book will be doing its job.